MATHEMATICAL PHYSICS SERIES

Editor: G. Stephenson, B.Sc., Ph.D., D.I.C.

Department of Mathematics, Imperial College, London

ELECTRIC AND MAGNETIC FORCES

Electric and Magnetic Forces

R. R. BIRSS
B.Sc., Ph.D., D.I.C., F.Inst.P., C.Eng., M.I.E.E.
Senior Lecturer in the School of Mathematical and Physical Sciences,
University of Sussex

1724

LONGMANS

LONGMANS, GREEN AND CO LTD
48 Grosvenor Street, London W1

Associated companies, branches and representatives throughout the world

First published 1967

Printed in Great Britain by
W. & G. Baird, Ltd., Belfast

CONTENTS

5. The Prediction of E_{ij}^{o}

6. The Prediction of E_{ij}^{*}

PREFACE

All electromagnetic devices that do mechanical work depend for their operation on the forces that arise in the presence of electric and magnetic fields. In simple cases the forces act directly on or between electrical charges—at rest, as in the quadrant electrometer, or in relative motion, as in the familiar domestic television tube. Other devices (e.g. galvanometers) rely on the forces between two or more closed electrical circuits carrying current, and here it is possible to use various alternative formulae for the force between current elements, each of which predicts the force on a complete circuit correctly. However, there are many electromagnetic devices that utilise the forces exerted on polarized or magnetized matter, obvious examples being ordinary relays and electric motors. These *ponderomotive* forces form the subject of the present book: the problem discussed is, in essence, the following. What is the total force (and torque) acting on a polarizable body in an electric field, or a magnetizable body in a magnetic field, and how is this force distributed within and over the body?

Specifying the *location* of ponderomotive forces is much the more difficult part of the problem because the topic is essentially an interdisciplinary one. It originates with the engineer who is interested in electromechanical energy transfer, but it involves the concepts and techniques both of continuum mechanics, which is familiar to an applied mathematician, and of ferromagnetic domain theory, which is the province of the solid state physicist. A successful treatment is one that brings together the relevant ideas from these three separate specialist disciplines: the viewpoint adopted in this book is that it is desirable to accept information from any available source, so that, for example, results derived from microscopic theory will not be rejected—as they sometimes are in continuum mechanics—just *because* they have been deduced microscopically. The interdisciplinary nature of the subject has also, in the past, been the origin of some confusion—real and semantic. For example, mathematicians and engineers have often failed to realise that a magnetic material differs from a continuum in that it is divided up into small regions, or domains, each of which is magnetized to saturation. Whilst this realisation is important it does not lead—as is sometimes supposed—to a facile solution of the problem. It is not feasible to dispense with the familiar framework provided by continuum mechanics; and to consider in detail the domain theory appropriate to a polycrystalline aggregate of single-crystal grains merely results in the wood being obscured by the trees. However, the existence of domains must be kept continually in mind—there is no merit in asserting that the wood does not consist of trees! Physicists, on the other hand, have often been slow to appreciate the practical importance of predictions of ponderomotive forces, since they become aware of the problem only occasionally through, for example, the mechanical failure of a device employing large magnetic fields, such as a synchrotron.

Because of the widespread use of rotating electrical machinery of all types, electrical engineers are, of course, more aware of the problem of 'forces on iron parts'. Some extremely large machines are in use nowadays and manufacturers are understandably reluctant to publicise breakdowns, but there are two types of failure that occur in practice. First, if the rotor becomes displaced from its central position, the total ponderomotive force will be non-zero and may be of sufficient magnitude to 'pull over' the rotor bringing it into contact with the stator, so that mechanical damage and possibly failure follow immediately. This phenomenon is usually initiated by wear or deflection on one or more bearings, and it is important, for example, in large induction machines and high-frequency inductor alternators. Secondly, even when the total ponderomotive force is zero, the force distribution may be such as to lead to failure of parts of the machine. The rotor is, of course, very rigidly constructed but breakages sometimes occur in parts of the stator: the fracture of interpole bolts of traction motors and the fatigue failure of laminations in the stator teeth of large hydrogenerators may be cited as examples. Mechanical resonance is usually important—as it is in the associated problem of noise.

Both electric and magnetic ponderomotive forces are considered but where, for convenience, attention has been concentrated on only one case, the magnetic situation—being, in general, the more difficult—has been chosen. To preserve the symmetry between the treatments of electricity and of magnetism, the pole-strength magnetization $\mathbf{I} = \mathbf{B} - \mu_o\mathbf{H}$ (weber m^{-2}) is used rather than the current-loop magnetization $\mathbf{M} = \mathbf{I}/\mu_o$ (ampere m^{-1}): rationalised m.k.s. units are used throughout. The relative permittivity, $\varepsilon_r = \varepsilon/\varepsilon_o$, and permeability, $\mu_r = \mu/\mu_o$, are not assumed to be constant (or infinite) and are taken, even when not explicitly stated, to be field dependent, i.e. $\varepsilon_r = \varepsilon_r(E)$ and $\mu_r = \mu_r(H)$. In addition, the choice of material for discussion has been influenced by its potential application to polycrystalline bodies of ordinary 'soft' ferromagnetic substances, such as iron: a consideration of materials exhibiting permanent polarization or magnetization is therefore excluded.

CHAPTER 1

Introduction

1.1 Ponderomotive forces

When a piece of iron is placed in a magnetic field, it is, in general, subject to a force that will move the iron unless it is restrained. Such a force is known as a ponderomotive force. Ponderomotive forces are also exerted on dielectric bodies in electric fields. The material presented in this book refers to static fields only, and it is also assumed that the dielectric or magnetic material is isotropic. A consideration of single crystals and other anisotropic bodies is thus specifically excluded. For convenience, the electric and magnetic cases are treated separately. A problem in which a body that is both dielectric and magnetic is placed in a combined electric and magnetic field must therefore be solved by superposition† of the results for a dielectric body in an electric field and a magnetic body in a magnetic field. When, as in these introductory remarks, it is not necessary to distinguish between the electric and magnetic cases, they will be treated together by referring to the ponderomotive force on a material body in a field.

The interaction between a material body and the field in which it is placed results not only in a tendency for the body to move but also in the body being put into a state of stress. Since all solid materials possess some degree of elasticity this leads to the material being strained—that is, it leads to a deformation of the body. A complete description of the ponderomotive force should therefore include a specification of how the force is distributed throughout the body, although the total ponderomotive force is often the quantity of practical interest. The force distribution depends, of course, on the electric or magnetic field conditions at points within the body.

---

† Materials that exhibit the unusual magneto-electric effect (Birss 1964) are excluded from consideration.

1.2 Maxwell's field equations

When a material body of arbitrary shape is placed in a known field, the field pattern is modified by the introduction of the body and the specification of the resulting field conditions can itself be quite a formidable problem. The field conditions are completely specified when solutions (satisfying the appropriate boundary conditions) have been obtained to the familiar Maxwell's equations

$$\operatorname{curl} \mathbf{E} = -\frac{\partial \mathbf{B}}{\partial t}, \tag{1a}$$

$$\operatorname{div} \mathbf{D} = \rho, \tag{1b}$$

$$\operatorname{curl} \mathbf{H} = \mathbf{J} + \frac{\partial \mathbf{D}}{\partial t}, \tag{1c}$$

$$\operatorname{div} \mathbf{B} = 0. \tag{1d}$$

The solution of these equations is possible only if additional *constitutive* relations are available connecting **D** to **E**, **J** to **E** and **B** to **H**, such as $\mathbf{D} = \varepsilon_r \varepsilon_o \mathbf{E}$, $\mathbf{J} = \sigma \mathbf{E}$, $\mathbf{B} = \mu_r \mu_o \mathbf{H}$ for a linear isotropic material, or some more general relations for a non-linear material. Maxwell's equations (1) constitute a set of coupled first-order partial differential equations connecting the various spatial components of the electric and magnetic vectors. They can sometimes be solved directly but it is often convenient to introduce potential functions and so obtain a smaller number of second-order equations, whilst satisfying some of Maxwell's equations identically.

For static fields, Maxwell's equations reduce to

$$\operatorname{curl} \mathbf{E} = 0, \tag{2a}$$

$$\operatorname{div} \mathbf{D} = \rho, \tag{2b}$$

$$\operatorname{curl} \mathbf{H} = \mathbf{J}, \tag{2c}$$

$$\operatorname{div} \mathbf{B} = 0, \tag{2d}$$

and the vector with the vanishing curl can be written as the (negative) gradient of a scalar potential, Φ, thus

$$\mathbf{E} = -\operatorname{grad} \Phi , \tag{3}$$

whilst the vector with the vanishing divergence can be written as the curl of a vector potential, **A**, thus

$$\mathbf{B} = \operatorname{curl} \mathbf{A} . \tag{4}$$

The definition of **E** and **B** in terms of Φ and **A** ensures that (2a) and (2d) are satisfied identically whilst (2b) and (2c) may be rewritten, in terms of the potentials Φ and **A**. It may be noted that, in contrast to equations (1), equations (2) do not couple together electrical and magnetic vectors: for *time-varying* fields the decoupling process is achieved—as indicated in section 2.3(c)—by exploiting the arbitrariness involved in the definitions of the potential functions. If the potentials Φ and **A** are known as functions of position throughout a region of space, the vectors **E** and **B** may be found from equations (3) and (4) whilst **D** and **H** may be found from the constitutive relations.

1.3 Solutions in free space

In free space, the potential Φ must satisfy the equation obtained by taking the divergence of both sides of (3), namely

$$\nabla^2 \Phi = -\frac{\rho}{\varepsilon_0}, \tag{5}$$

which is known as Poisson's equation. If a region is free of charges, the field being produced by charges that can be excluded from the region by closed surfaces drawn around them, then Poisson's equation reduces in the charge-free region to Laplace's equation,

$$\nabla^2 \Phi = 0 . \tag{6}$$

This is a second-order partial differential equation and its solution for each charge-free region contains two arbitrary functions that can be determined from a knowledge either of the potential at all surfaces or of the potential and the first (spatial) derivatives of the potential at a selected number of surfaces. A solution to equation (6) that satisfies the prescribed boundary conditions gives the value of the potential Φ at every point of the region. An alternative approach is to express Φ as an integral, over a volume V containing all the charges, of a function that involves the charge density ρ. Thus a volume element dV, the position of which is defined by a vector **r**, contains a charge $\rho\, dV$ and its contribution to the potential is, from Coulomb's law,

$$d\Phi = \frac{\rho\, dV}{4\pi\varepsilon_o r}. \tag{7}$$

The total potential due to all the charges is therefore

$$\Phi = \iiint_V \frac{\rho\, dV}{4\pi\varepsilon_o r}, \tag{8}$$

and this formula can be generalised to include a number of bodies and also surface distributions of charge.

In free space, the vector potential **A** must satisfy the equation obtained by taking the curl of both sides of (4), namely

$$\text{curl}\,\text{curl}\,\mathbf{A} \equiv \text{grad}\,\text{div}\,\mathbf{A} - \nabla^2\mathbf{A} = \mu_o\mathbf{J}. \tag{9}$$

Now the divergence of the vector potential **A** is not determined uniquely by equation (4) and div **A** is undefined to the extent of the addition of an arbitrary function of position (see 2.3(c)). For static fields it is customary to make the simplest choice and to set div **A** = 0, since this can be done without altering equation (4). Equation (9) may therefore be written in the form

$$\Delta\mathbf{A} = -\mu_o\mathbf{J}, \tag{10}$$

where the Laplacian operator $\Delta \equiv \nabla^2$ is defined, in curvilinear coordinates by the identity in (9). In Cartesian coordinate systems, however, $\Delta\mathbf{A} \equiv \nabla^2\mathbf{A}$ is a vector the components of which are obtained by operating with ∇^2 on the three components of **A**. The solution of equation (10) subject to arbitrary boundary conditions is usually considerably more complicated than the solution of Laplace's equation (6), because the three components of **A** are not independent but are connected by the equation div **A** = 0. In fact, in the magnetic case it is distinctly advantageous to work with the alternative integral expression obtained from the free-space form of

Biot and Savart's law. For a filamentary circuit l carrying a current i,

$$\mathbf{B} = \frac{\mu_o}{4\pi} i \oint \frac{\mathbf{r} \wedge d\mathbf{l}}{r^3} \tag{11a}$$

and, for a volume distribution of current,

$$\mathbf{B} = -\frac{\mu_o}{4\pi} \iiint_V \mathbf{J} \times \operatorname{grad} r^{-1}\, dV, \tag{11b}$$

so that the vector potential is given by†

$$\mathbf{A} = \frac{\mu_o}{4\pi} \iiint_V \frac{J}{r} dV. \tag{12}$$

The integrals in equations (8) and (12) are often tedious to evaluate but they represent a method of solution that is suitable for use when a digital computer is available.

1.4 Solutions in the presence of material bodies

If dielectric or magnetic bodies are present, it is only for a few very idealized problems that equations (2) can be solved with any degree of simplicity. Analytic methods, such as those using conformal transformations, do not often lead to solutions in closed form, and solutions in terms of infinite series must converge fairly rapidly to be useful. The practical problems in which the boundary conditions are simple enough to permit an analytic solution (Hauge 1929, Weber 1950, Bewley 1948) are not numerous and are effectively confined to two-dimensional problems. For practical applications experimental and numerical methods of mapping fields have been devised, as well as graphical and semi-graphical procedures involving some calculations.

Perhaps the two best-known approaches are finite-difference methods (Allen 1954, Shaw 1953, Southwell 1940, 1946, 1956) and the electrolytic tank analogue method (Diggle and Harthill 1954). In a

† Equations (12) and (8) are discussed further below.

finite-difference method, the differential equation for a potential is replaced by many finite-difference equations which take the form of linear equations connecting the potential at one of a finite number of regularly spaced points, or nodes, with the potentials at other nodes close to it. Trial values of the potentials at the nodes are then successively improved by considering the effects at adjacent points of a change in the potential at a particular node. Non-linearity in a constitutive relation can be accommodated by a process of successive approximation or, more usually, by replacing the constitutive relation by two or more linear relations. In the case of the magnetization of iron bodies, for example, saturation is often important, and this can be allowed for in an approximate fashion by replacing the magnetization curve (B versus H) with a similarly shaped curve constructed by connecting two or more straight line segments of differing slopes. In the electrolytic tank analogue method, advantage is taken of the analogy between the electric field produced by a point charge and the pattern of flow of current in a conducting electrolytic solution when current is fed into it at a corresponding point. Since the current is subject to the continuity equation

$$\operatorname{div} \mathbf{J} + \frac{\partial \rho}{\partial t} = 0\,, \tag{13}$$

where $\partial\rho/\partial t$ is zero except at points at which current is being fed into (or removed from) the electrolyte, there is a direct analogy with equation (2b). The electrolytic tank method can thus readily be used to predict the electric field due to a collection of point charges or a distribution of charges. It can also be used to determine the magnetic field due to a collection of line currents, provided that the problem is sensibly two-dimensional, for it is then possible to interchange the roles of lines of force and lines of equipotential in the analogue. An advantage of the method is that in two-dimensional problems it is possible to allow for non-linearity in a constitutive relation by using a tank in which the depth of electrolyte varies from place to place.

The specification of the field conditions that result when a material body of arbitrary shape is placed in a known field can be, as mentioned above, quite a formidable problem, and it will not be pursued further here. There is an extensive coverage of this problem in the literature† and it will be assumed in what follows that the field conditions can always be determined uniquely at points outside and within the body. The problem of interest therefore is to specify the distribution of ponderomotive force in terms of these known field conditions.

1.5 Vector fields and their singularities

Having taken for granted that a solution—exact or approximate—can always be found to the static form (2) of Maxwell's equations, it is desirable to consider what is involved in specifying field conditions within a material body by the four vectors **E**, **D**, **H** and **B**, and indeed why four are necessary rather than just one electrical and one magnetic vector. In free space there is no need to distinguish between the two electric vectors **E** and **D** or between the two magnetic vectors **H** and **B**. Moreover, a simple consideration of static electric and magnetic fields reveals a difference between them in that they exhibit different sorts of singularities. A graphical display, or field plot, of the lines of force can reveal (in a favourably orientated cross-section) two sorts of singularities typified by the diagrams shown in Fig. 1.1. These are both singularities in the field, and

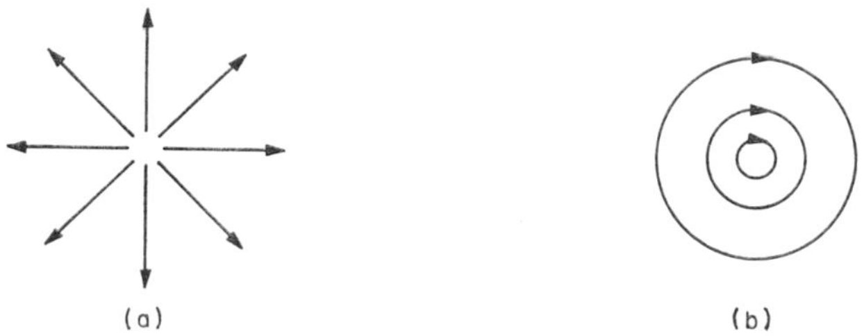

Fig. 1.1

appear to act in some way as *origins* of the field. A singularity of type (a) will be referred to as a source and a singularity of type (b) as a vortex. It is a matter of experiment that sources are typical of

† Interested readers may care to consult, for example, the book by K. J. Binns and P. J. Lawrenson, *Analysis and Computation of Electric and Magnetic Field Problems*, Pergamon Press, 1963.

electric fields and are associated with the presence of charge whereas vortices are typical of magnetic fields (produced electromagnetically) and are associated with current.† Of course, both an indefinitely small single charge and an indefinitely thin wire carrying current are idealizations, but they are idealizations that are approximately realized in practice. It is possible, for example, to experiment not only with small charged material bodies but also with very small fundamental particles (electrons, protons, etc.) that carry discrete quantities of charge, whilst the approximation of neglecting the thickness of a conductor carrying current is a common one in electrical engineering. It may be mentioned in passing that the laws relating fields to charges and line currents, once obtained, can be readily extended to deal with surface and volume distributions of charge and current.

The *strength* of a source or a vortex is a measure of how much of the field originates at the singularity. If Fig. 1.1(a) represents lines of force in some vector field **F** (for example, $\mathbf{F} \equiv \mathbf{E}$), the strength of the source depends on how many lines radiate outwards from the singularity. Remembering that Fig. 1.1(a) is a two-dimensional representation of a source in three dimensions, it may be seen that a geometrically reasonable definition of the strength of a source is given by

$$s' = \oiint_S \mathbf{F} \, . \, d\mathbf{S}, \tag{14}$$

where S is a closed surface surrounding the singularity. However, many sources may be present simultaneously, so it is customary to replace s' by a source density $s = s'/V$, where V is the volume enclosed by the surface S, and to proceed to the limit when the volume contracts whilst still containing the singularity. The source density s is therefore defined by the equation

$$s = \lim_{V \to 0} \left[\frac{1}{V} \oiint_S \mathbf{F} \, . \, d\mathbf{S} \right] \equiv \operatorname{div} \mathbf{F} \, . \tag{15}$$

† See 1.6 for a discussion of the existence of magnetic monopoles.

Similarly, if Fig. 1.1(b) represents lines of force in a vector field **F** (for example, $\mathbf{F} \equiv \mathbf{H}$), the strength of the vortex depends on the strength of the field circulating around the singularity. If Σ is an area in the plane of the cross section represented in the figure (the plane of the paper), a geometrically reasonable definition of the strength of a vortex in that plane is given by

$$c'_\Sigma = \oint_l \mathbf{F} \cdot d\mathbf{l}, \tag{16}$$

where l is a closed path bounding the area Σ. Proceeding to the limit, as before, with c'_Σ replaced by a surface density $c_\Sigma = c'_\Sigma/\Sigma$, gives

$$c_\Sigma = \lim_{\Sigma \to 0} \left[\frac{1}{\Sigma} \oint_l \mathbf{F} \cdot d\mathbf{l} \right]. \tag{17}$$

But the right-hand side of (17) is, by definition, the component in the direction normal to Σ of the vector curl **F**. The strength of a vortex or vortex distribution is therefore properly specified by a vector, **c**, the three components of which are given by expressions like (17). This vector is called the circulation density† and is, of course, defined by the equation

$$\mathbf{c} = \operatorname{curl} \mathbf{F}. \tag{18}$$

It is a general result, not peculiar to electrical and magnetic phenomena, that any vector **F** is uniquely defined when its source density $s = \operatorname{div} \mathbf{F}$ and its circulation density $\mathbf{c} = \operatorname{curl} \mathbf{F}$ are prescribed at all points in space, provided that the totality of singularities, as well as the source and circulation densities are zero at infinity. In fact, s and **c** determine **F** at any point according to the formula

$$\mathbf{F} = -\operatorname{grad} \Phi_F + \operatorname{curl} \mathbf{A}_F, \tag{19a}$$

where Φ_F and $\mathbf{A}_F$ are given by

$$\Phi_F = \frac{1}{4\pi} \iiint_V \frac{s}{r} \, dV \tag{19b}$$

† If **F** is the velocity of a particle, as in the kinematics of continuous media, the vector curl **F** is often called the vorticity.

and

$$\mathbf{A}_F = \frac{1}{4\pi}\iiint\limits_V \frac{\mathbf{c}}{r} dV. \tag{19c}$$

Equations (19) constitute what is often called Helmholtz's theorem: formal proofs may be found in many textbooks on electromagnetism but a particularly detailed discussion is given by Panofsky and Phillips (1955), who also demonstrate that (19) is a unique solution for **F**.

1.6 The four electric and magnetic vectors

As stated above, any vector field **F** is completely described by a specification of the source density $s = \text{div}\,\mathbf{F}$ and the circulation density $\mathbf{c} = \text{curl}\,\mathbf{F}$. In free space, Maxwell's equations (2) are in conformity with such a specification, for the constitutive relations are linear and ε_o and μ_o are constants, so that (2) may be written in the form

$$\begin{aligned} \text{curl}\,\mathbf{E} &= 0, \\ \text{div}\,\mathbf{E} &= \rho/\varepsilon_o, \\ \text{curl}\,\mathbf{B} &= \mu_o\mathbf{J}, \\ \text{div}\,\mathbf{B} &= 0. \end{aligned} \tag{20}$$

Equation (20) specifies one electric vector and one magnetic vector in terms of its source density and its circulation density, and equations (8) and (12) giving the integral forms of the potentials Φ and **A** follow directly from (19a) and (19b) respectively without the need of invoking Coulomb's law and Biot and Savart's law.

Since curl $\mathbf{E} = 0$, a static electric field exhibits no singularities of the type shown in Fig. 1.1(b). Similarly, since div $\mathbf{B} = 0$, a static magnetic field exhibits no singularities of the type shown in Fig. 1.1(a). A formulation of magnetostatics in which a singularity of type (a) is associated with magnetic monopoles is inappropriate in the absence of extended magnetic materials because it is believed (Sandars 1966) that monopoles do not exist in free space. Although a progressive subdivision of matter into successively smaller volumes is consistent with the existence of a singularity of type (a) identified with charge, such a process of successive subdivision never yields a singularity of type (a) associated with magnetic polarity. What is obtained is a singularity of *dipole* form which could, in principle, be due either to the presence of two poles of opposite sign close together or to the presence of a small (Ampèrian) current loop. The former alternative is a doublet that corresponds to two singularities of type (a) whilst the current loop corresponds to a special form of the singularity of type (b). Experiments on the passage of elementary particles, particularly neutrons, through matter indicate that even in material media the elementary dipoles behave like Ampèrian current loops rather than two monopoles in close proximity (Hughes 1953). In both free space and material media, therefore, experiment suggests that the fundamental origins of electric and magnetic fields are charge and the motion of charge.

In the presence of material bodies, however, equations (20) are replaced by equations (2) and these do not in themselves provide a complete specification of the *four* vectors **E**, **D**, **H** and **B**. Equations (2) prescribe only the source densities of **D** and **B** and the circulation densities of **E** and **H**. It is true that additional restrictions are placed on the electric and magnetic vectors because of the existence of constitutive relations, but the situation is obviously quite different from the ideal one in which the four vectors are specified by four source densities and four circulation densities. It is therefore desirable to investigate the physical significance of the four vectors—and indeed to enquire why four are necessary when two suffice in free space.

Consider the case in which the charge density ρ and current density **J** are specified not in free space but in a material medium of infinite extent which is characterised by constant permeability and permittivity. The curl of **D** and the divergence of **H** are then both zero, from (2a) and (2d), so that **D** and **H** are everywhere specified by their source and circulation densities. When it is remembered that ρ is the free, or extrinsic, charge density and **J** the extrinsic current density, the physical singificance of **D** and **H** becomes clear in this case. They are auxiliary vectors representing the fields $\varepsilon_o\mathbf{E}$ and $\mathbf{B}/\mu_o$ that would exist if the material media were removed whilst the charge and current densities, ρ and **J**, were preserved unchanged. For static fields, **D** and **H** must conform to equations (2b) and (2c) or, alternatively, to the integral form of these equations, namely Gauss' law

$$\oiint_S \mathbf{D} \cdot d\mathbf{S} = q \tag{21}$$

and Ampère's circuital law

$$\oint_l \mathbf{H} \cdot d\mathbf{l} = Ni, \tag{22}$$

where q is the total free charge enclosed by the closed surface S and i is the current in each of N turns linked with the closed path l. Since **D** and **H** are related in the above example to the situation when the material medium is removed, presumably the other two vectors, **E** and **B**, represent in some way the electric and magnetic fields within material media. But how are such fields to be defined? It is impossible, for example, to place a test charge within a material body to determine the electric field at interior points.

To answer this question it is necessary to consider the molecular nature of solid matter. The important characteristic of solid matter in this connection is that matter is essentially free space plus charge. Without entering into a detailed discussion of the fundamental particles that comprise solid materials, it can be affirmed that matter is essentially charges in motion in free space. If the charged regions are assumed to be of conventional (molecular) sizes then the majority of the volume of a solid is, in fact, intermolecular free space. This picture of matter as being free space plus charge, due originally to H. A. Lorentz (1909), possesses two considerable advantages. First, it implies that all electrical and magnetic phenomena are correctly described by (20) rather than by (2), and secondly, any non-linearity implicit in the constitutive relation is removed and the principle of superposition can be applied to both electric and magnetic fields. It has, however, a serious disadvantage in that the electric and magnetic vectors fluctuate rapidly on a microscopic scale—that is over distances comparable with the intermolecular separation—and it is convenient to denote these microscopic vectors by the symbols **e** and **b** to distinguish them from the corresponding macroscopic vectors **E** and **B** which do not fluctuate on this scale. In the simple example discussed above of an extended medium with constant permeability and permittivity, the auxiliary vectors **D** and

H do not, of course, vary rapidly in this fashion because they originate from the extrinsic densities ρ and **J**. Furthermore, since superposition is applicable, the vectors **D** and **H** are, in fact, partial fields, that is $\mathbf{D}/\varepsilon_o$ and $\mu_o\mathbf{H}$ are the (constant) contributions to the true, rapidly varying fields **e** and **b** arising solely from the extrinsic densities ρ and **J**.

When a solid material body is introduced into an electric or magnetic field it is no longer possible to obtain measurements from within the material and, at points outside the body, it is observed that the field has been enhanced or reduced by the presence of the body, as if some of the field now originates from within the body. This is ascribed to an internal rearrangement of its (initially neutral) distributions of intrinsic charge and currents, and this constitutes the (electrical) polarization or magnetization. The total fields **e** and **b** would be given by equations (20)—with the time derivatives restored—if ρ and **J** were replaced by the total charge density ω and the total current density **j**, which include the charges comprising the solid material as well as the extrinsic quantities. Although neither ω and **j** nor the rapidly varying fields **e** and **b** are accessible to direct observation, the averages of the electric and magnetic vectors over large distances are, and this is most readily appreciated by considering the two particularly simple experimental arrangements shown in Fig. 1.2.

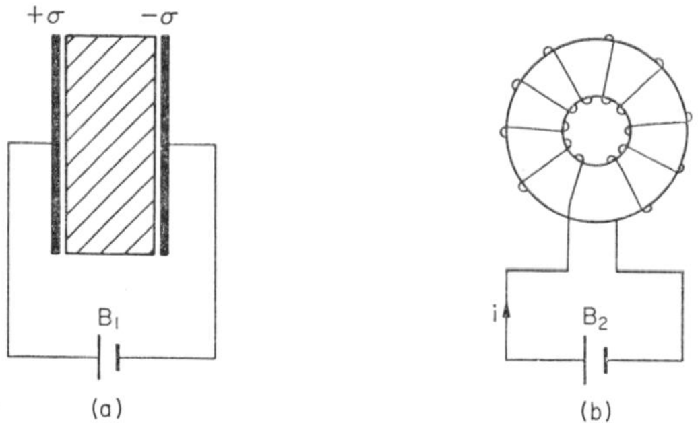

Fig. 1.2

Fig. 1.2(a) is a diagrammatic representation of a parallel plate capacitor completely filled with a dielectric and with a charge of surface density σ maintained on the plates by a battery B_1, and

Fig. 1.2(b) is a similar representation of a toroidal iron-cored inductor, of N turns, supplied with a current i by a battery B_2. The capacitor plates are assumed to be close together and of large area so that fringe effects can be neglected. Hence, within the dielectric, the displacement, **D**, is specified by a constant vector perpendicular to the plates. The inner and outer 'radii' of the inductor are assumed to be much bigger than the difference between them and the iron core is assumed to be of high permeability. Leakage fields can therefore be neglected and the magnetic field, **H**, within the iron can be specified by a circumferential magnetic vector that is constant across any cross-section of the iron and everywhere perpendicular to a 'radial' direction.

The magnitudes of **D** and **H** may be determined as follows. Gauss' law may be applied, in the usual way, to a pill-box shaped surface at the surface of the dielectric to give the result $D = \sigma$. Also, Ampère's circuital law may be applied to a circumferential path within the iron and threading the toroidal coil to give the result $2\pi aH = Ni$, where a is the mean 'radius' of the toroid. In this way **D** and **H** are specified everywhere within the dielectric and the iron respectively. Now although the rapidly varying vectors **e** and **b** cannot be observed directly it is possible to obtain experimental information on effective or space-average values of electrical and magnetic vectors within matter. In the capacitor, for example, it is true that a test charge cannot be placed within the dielectric to determine **e**, but it is possible to imagine that a test charge be taken from one plate to the other via the rest of the circuit and therefore through the battery B_1, or any other device that maintains the potential difference, v, between the plates. In free space the vector $\mathbf{E} = \mathbf{D}/\varepsilon_0$ would be related to v by the equation

$$v = \int_a^b \mathbf{E} \, . \, d\mathbf{l}, \tag{23}$$

where v is the potential difference between the two points a and b. Since the work done in taking unit charge from one plate to the other (at infinitesimal speed) via the battery B_1 is v, the result of dividing v by the plate separation can therefore be looked upon as an effective value of **e**, that is a value obtained by averaging along a path running directly from one plate to the other. It is a matter of experiment that this value, **E**, is ε_r times smaller than the free-space value $\mathbf{D}/\varepsilon_o$ (and that the relative permittivity ε_r varies from one dielectric to another). In a similar way a single-turn secondary coil of area S can be wound around the toroid of Fig. 1.2(b) and the e.m.f. induced when the current i is established provides information on the space-average value of a magnetic vector within the iron. In free space, the rate of change of the vector $\mathbf{B} = \mu_o\mathbf{H}$ would be related to this e.m.f. by Faraday's law

$$\text{e.m.f.} = -\frac{d}{dt}\iint_S \mathbf{B}\,.\,d\mathbf{S}. \tag{24}$$

Thus the value obtained (with an integrating instrument such as a fluxmeter) for the integral of the e.m.f. with respect to time can be looked upon as determining an effective value of **b**, that is a value obtained by averaging over a cross-section of the iron toroid, and it is a matter of experiment that this value, **B**, is μ_r times larger than the free-space value $\mu_o\mathbf{H}$.

It is in this sense that **E** and **B** may be regarded as the fundamental vectors rather than **D** and **H** and it is to secure agreement with experiment that it is assumed that these effective fields **E** and **B** obey *local* constitutive relations of the form

$$\begin{aligned} \mathbf{D} &= \varepsilon\mathbf{E} = \varepsilon_r\varepsilon_o\mathbf{E}, \\ \mathbf{B} &= \mu\mathbf{H} = \mu_r\mu_o\mathbf{H}. \end{aligned} \tag{25}$$

It is important to realise, however, that the simple interpretation of **D** and **H** as partial fields is true only in special circumstances. The obvious example is that in which the only matter present is in the form of an infinitely extended material medium of constant permeability and permittivity. In all other cases the symmetry of the geometry of the experimental arrangement must similarly be high enough (as in the parallel plate capacitor and the toroidal inductor) to permit **D** to be derived from (21) alone or **H** to be derived from (22) alone. The high degree of symmetry then enables **D** to be specified by only its source density and **H** to be specified by only its circulation density. To take an obvious example in which **D** can not be regarded as a partial field, consider the pattern of lines of force appropriate to a single charge placed near a plane surface of an extensive dielectric body of high permittivity. The electric field

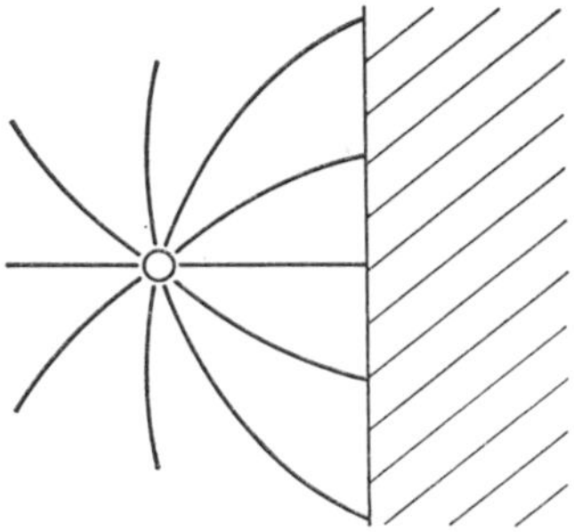

Fig. 1.3

outside the body looks somewhat as shown in Fig. 1.3, and it is obvious that the pattern of lines of **E**—and therefore of **D**—does not correspond to the partial field of the single charge in free space when the dielectric is removed.

It is instructive to use equations (25) to write down the source and circulation densities that are not specified by Maxwell's equations (2), thus

$$\operatorname{div}\mathbf{E} = \operatorname{div}\left[\frac{\mathbf{D}}{\varepsilon}\right] = \frac{1}{\varepsilon}\operatorname{div}\mathbf{D} + \mathbf{D}\,.\operatorname{grad}\left[\frac{1}{\varepsilon}\right] = \frac{\rho}{\varepsilon} + \mathbf{D}\,.\operatorname{grad}\left[\frac{1}{\varepsilon}\right],$$

$$\operatorname{curl}\mathbf{D} = \operatorname{curl}(\varepsilon\mathbf{E}) = \varepsilon\operatorname{curl}\mathbf{E} - \mathbf{E}\times\operatorname{grad}\varepsilon = -\mathbf{E}\times\operatorname{grad}\varepsilon, \quad (26a)$$

and

$$\operatorname{div}\mathbf{H} = \operatorname{div}\left[\frac{\mathbf{B}}{\mu}\right] = \frac{1}{\mu}\operatorname{div}\mathbf{B} + \mathbf{B}\,.\operatorname{grad}\left[\frac{1}{\mu}\right] = \mathbf{B}\,.\operatorname{grad}\left[\frac{1}{\mu}\right], \quad (26b)$$

$$\operatorname{curl}\mathbf{B} = \operatorname{curl}(\mu\mathbf{H}) = \mu\operatorname{curl}\mathbf{H} - \mathbf{H}\times\operatorname{grad}\mu = \mu\mathbf{J} - \mathbf{H}\times\operatorname{grad}\mu\,.$$

For dielectric materials ε_r is usually constant, but even then the terms in grad ε and grad ε^{-1} in (26a) do not necessarily vanish everywhere, for they have, in general, finite values over surfaces separating two dielectrics. It is, of course, this fact that makes the pattern of lines of force shown in Fig. 1.3 different from that appropriate to free space. For magnetic materials μ_r depends on position even within the material medium, and the additional source and circulation densities are given by (26b). The application of Gauss' law and Ampère's circuital law to both free space and to the interior of a material body implies, of course, that in free space **D**, and not **E**, originates at a source and that **H** and not **B** originates at a vortex. This explains the position of the factors ε_0 and μ_0 in Coulomb's law and Biot and Savart's law respectively. (It may be noted that if magnetic monopoles were admitted these would be sources of **B**.)

By dealing with the vectors **E** and **B** which represent space-averages of vectors that are not themselves constant within matter, the material medium is regarded, not as a vacuum full of sources or vortices, but as a medium in which the two field vectors are everywhere related by a local constitutive equation of the form (25). The rapidly-varying nature of the vectors **e** or **b** is thereby suppressed to leave two slowly-varying field vectors that are everywhere connected by a scalar permittivity or permeability. The sources and vortices are therefore represented in terms of differential equations that have to be solved simultaneously inside and outside the material medium. However, to put this procedure on a rigorous basis it is necessary to look more closely at the averaging process referred to above and this is considered in detail in 2.3 of the next chapter.

CHAPTER 2

The Total Ponderomotive Force

2.1 The force on a single charge

Before proceeding to consider the total ponderomotive force on a material body in a field, it is helpful to consider the simple example of the force between two point charges in a vacuum. Consider two ideal point charges of strength q_1 and q_2 situated at A and B as shown in Fig. 2.1(a). The force acting on q_1 due to the presence of

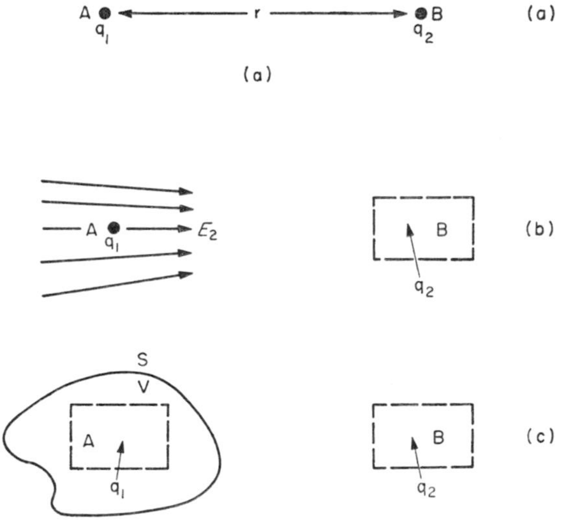

Fig. 2.1

q_2 is, of course, $q_1q_2/4\pi\varepsilon_o r^2$ in the direction BA. However, if the conditions at A are under discussion it is inconvenient to have to refer also to conditions at B and so it is customary to introduce as an auxiliary concept the electric field vector. If $\mathbf{E}_1$ is the field due to q_1 alone and $\mathbf{E}_2$ that due to q_2 alone then the total field is $\mathbf{E} = \mathbf{E}_1 + \mathbf{E}_2$ since the charges are in a vacuum. Furthermore, the force on q_1

due to the presence of q_2 is given by

$$\mathbf{F} = q_1\mathbf{E} = q_1(\mathbf{E}_1 + \mathbf{E}_2) \tag{1a}$$

or, since q_1 does not experience any force due to its self field, by

$$\mathbf{F} = q_1\mathbf{E}_2 . \tag{1b}$$

The charge q_2 has thus been replaced by its field in the sense that the force is assumed to be transmitted by the field, and it is no longer necessary to know the *location* of the charge q_2—a situation that is depicted symbolically in Fig. 2.1(b). However, a further step can be taken: it is also possible to dispense with the knowledge of the location of q_1 provided the value of $\mathbf{E} = \mathbf{E}_1 + \mathbf{E}_2$ is known over any surface that encloses q_1 but not q_2.

Let q_1, but not q_2, be surrounded by a closed surface S enclosing a volume V, as shown in Fig. 2.1(c). From Gauss' law, the electric displacements $\mathbf{D}_1$ and $\mathbf{D}_2$ corresponding to $\mathbf{E}_1$ and $\mathbf{E}_2$ are subject to the relationships

$$\oint\!\!\oint_S \mathbf{D}_1 . d\mathbf{S} = q_1 , \tag{2a}$$

$$\oint\!\!\oint_S \mathbf{D}_2 . d\mathbf{S} = 0 , \tag{2b}$$

so that

$$q_1 = \oint\!\!\oint_S (\mathbf{D}_1 + \mathbf{D}_2) . d\mathbf{S} = \oint\!\!\oint_S \mathbf{D} . d\mathbf{S} . \tag{3}$$

Also, the Gauss divergence theorem allows equation (3) to be written in the form

$$q_1 = \iiint_V \operatorname{div} \mathbf{D} \, dV, \tag{4}$$

a result that is immediately obvious for distributed charge† from

† It is perhaps easier to think not of a point charge but of a very high (but finite) concentration of charge within a very small volume, because the infinite discontinuities in the field $\mathbf{E}_1$ at A are thereby avoided.

Maxwell's equation div $\mathbf{D} = \rho$ and the relationship

$$q_1 = \iiint_V \rho \, dV. \tag{5}$$

From (1b), the force on q_1 due to the presence of q_2 is thus

$$\mathbf{F} = q_1(\mathbf{E})_A = (\mathbf{E})_A \iiint_V \operatorname{div} \mathbf{D} \, dV, \tag{6}$$

where $(\mathbf{E})_A$ is the value of the total electric field evaluated at the point A. However, div $\mathbf{D}$ is zero everywhere within S except at the point A, where $\mathbf{E}_A$ is evaluated. Thus $\mathbf{E}_A$ may be taken inside the integral signs and the restriction on the point of evaluation removed, so that

$$\mathbf{F} = \iiint_V \mathbf{E} \operatorname{div} \mathbf{D} \, dV. \tag{7}$$

This integral may now be represented in terms of surface integrals, since each of the three components of the vector $\mathbf{E}$ div $\mathbf{D}$ may be expressed as the divergence of a vector. For example, consider the x-component of $\mathbf{F}$, that is

$$F_x = \iiint_V E_x \operatorname{div} \mathbf{D} \, dV = \iiint_V E_x \varepsilon_o \left[\frac{\partial E_x}{\partial x} + \frac{\partial E_y}{\partial y} + \frac{\partial E_z}{\partial z} \right] dV. \tag{8}$$

The divergence of a vector $\mathbf{U}$ with components

$$\begin{aligned} U_x &= \tfrac{1}{2}\varepsilon_o(E_x^2 - E_y^2 - E_z^2), \\ U_y &= \varepsilon_o E_x E_y, \\ U_z &= \varepsilon_o E_x E_z, \end{aligned} \tag{9a}$$

is given by

$$\begin{aligned} \frac{\partial U_x}{\partial x} + \frac{\partial U_y}{\partial y} + \frac{\partial U_z}{\partial z} = \varepsilon_o \Big[& E_x \frac{\partial E_x}{\partial x} - E_y \frac{\partial E_y}{\partial x} - E_z \frac{\partial E_z}{\partial x} \\ & + E_x \frac{\partial E_y}{\partial y} + E_y \frac{\partial E_x}{\partial y} + E_x \frac{\partial E_z}{\partial z} + E_z \frac{\partial E_x}{\partial z} \Big]. \end{aligned} \tag{10}$$

However, from the electrostatic form of Maxwell's equation, curl $\mathbf{E} = 0$, or

$$\frac{\partial E_y}{\partial x} = \frac{\partial E_x}{\partial y} \tag{11a}$$

and

$$\frac{\partial E_z}{\partial x} = \frac{\partial E_x}{\partial z}, \tag{11b}$$

so that

$$\operatorname{div} \mathbf{U} = \varepsilon_o E_x \left[\frac{\partial E_x}{\partial x} + \frac{\partial E_y}{\partial y} + \frac{\partial E_z}{\partial z} \right], \tag{12}$$

and equation (8) may be written in the form

$$F_x = \iiint\limits_V \operatorname{div} \mathbf{U}\, dV = \oiint\limits_S \mathbf{U} \,.\, d\mathbf{S}. \tag{13a}$$

Similarly

$$F_y = \oiint\limits_S \mathbf{U}' \,.\, d\mathbf{S} \tag{13b}$$

and

$$F_z = \oiint\limits_S \mathbf{U}'' \,.\, d\mathbf{S}, \tag{13c}$$

where

$$\begin{aligned} U_x' &= \varepsilon_o E_y E_x, \\ U_y' &= \tfrac{1}{2}\varepsilon_o (E_y^2 - E_x^2 - E_z^2), \\ U_z' &= \varepsilon_o E_y E_z \end{aligned} \tag{9b}$$

and

$$\begin{aligned} U_x'' &= \varepsilon_o E_x E_z, \\ U_y'' &= \varepsilon_o E_y E_z, \\ U_z'' &= \tfrac{1}{2}\varepsilon_o (E_z^2 - E_x^2 - E_y^2). \end{aligned} \tag{9c}$$

A more simple expression for the force **F** on q_1 due to the presence of q_2 may be obtained by observing that, if $d\mathbf{S} = \mathbf{n}\,dS$,

$$F_x = \oiint_S \mathbf{U}.\mathbf{n}\,dS$$

$$= \oiint_S [U_x n_x + U_y n_y + U_z n_z]\,dS$$

$$= \oiint_S [\tfrac{1}{2}\varepsilon_o(E_x^2 - E_y^2 - E_z^2)n_x + \varepsilon_o E_x E_y n_y + \varepsilon_o E_x E_z n_z]\,dS$$

$$= \oiint_S \varepsilon_o[E_x(E_x n_x + E_y n_y + E_z n_z) - \tfrac{1}{2}(E_x^2 + E_y^2 + E_z^2)n_x]\,dS$$

$$= \oiint_S \varepsilon_o[\mathbf{E}(\mathbf{E}.\mathbf{n}) - \tfrac{1}{2}E^2\mathbf{n}]_x\,dS, \tag{14}$$

with similar expressions for F_y and F_z. Hence the force **F** itself is given by

$$\mathbf{F} = \oiint_S \varepsilon_o[\mathbf{E}(\mathbf{E}.\mathbf{n}) - \tfrac{1}{2}E^2\mathbf{n}]\,dS. \tag{15}$$

(This result can also be obtained by employing the relationship curl **E** = 0 to write equation (8) in the form

$$F_x = \iiint_V \varepsilon_o\left[\frac{\partial(E_x E_x)}{\partial x} + \frac{\partial(E_x E_y)}{\partial y} + \frac{\partial(E_x E_z)}{\partial z} - \frac{1}{2}\frac{\partial(E^2)}{\partial x}\right]dV \tag{16}$$

and then using the less-familiar corollary of the Gauss divergence theorem

$$\iiint_V \frac{\partial\phi}{\partial x}\,dV = \oiint_S \phi n_x\,dS, \tag{17}$$

where ϕ is a scalar, to obtain (14). Equation (17) is extremely useful in obtaining general transformations between vector and surface integrals.) An entirely similar analysis for the case of two magnetic point poles leads to the result

$$\mathbf{F} = \oiint_S \mu_o[\mathbf{H}(\mathbf{H}.\mathbf{n}) - \tfrac{1}{2}H^2\mathbf{n}]\,dS. \tag{18}$$

If the position of the charge q_1 is specified by the vector $\mathbf{r}$ (with components x, y, z), a similar procedure can be used to express the vector $\mathbf{r} \times \mathbf{F}$ as a surface integral. The physical significance of this vector is that, if q_1 is mechanically attached to the origin of coordinates in some way, $\mathbf{\Gamma} = \mathbf{r} \times \mathbf{F}$ is the total torque about the origin due to the presence of q_2. Thus, from (16)

$$\Gamma_x = [\mathbf{r} \times \mathbf{F}]_x = yF_z - zF_y$$

$$= y \iiint_V \varepsilon_o \left[\frac{\partial(E_xE_z)}{\partial x} + \frac{\partial(E_yE_z)}{\partial y} + \frac{\partial(E_z^2)}{\partial z} - \frac{1}{2}\frac{\partial(E^2)}{\partial z}\right] dV$$

$$- z \iiint_V \varepsilon_o \left[\frac{\partial(E_xE_y)}{\partial x} + \frac{\partial(E_y^2)}{\partial y} + \frac{\partial(E_yE_z)}{\partial z} - \frac{1}{2}\frac{\partial(E^2)}{\partial y}\right] dV$$

$$= \iiint_V \varepsilon_o \left[\frac{\partial}{\partial x}(yE_xE_z) + \frac{\partial}{\partial y}(yE_yE_z) + \frac{\partial}{\partial z}(yE_z^2) - \frac{1}{2}\frac{\partial}{\partial z}(yE^2)\right] dV$$

$$- \iiint_V \varepsilon_o \left[\frac{\partial}{\partial x}(zE_xE_y) + \frac{\partial}{\partial y}(zE_y^2) + \frac{\partial}{\partial z}(zE_yE_z) - \frac{1}{2}\frac{\partial}{\partial y}(zE^2)\right] dV, \tag{19}$$

and the volume integrals may be transformed to surface integrals with the aid of (17) to give

$$\Gamma_x = \oiint_S \varepsilon_o[(yE_z - zE_y)(\mathbf{E}.\mathbf{n}) - \tfrac{1}{2}E^2(yn_z - zn_y)]\,dS$$

$$= \oiint_S \varepsilon_o[(\mathbf{r} \times \mathbf{E})(\mathbf{E}.\mathbf{n}) - \tfrac{1}{2}E^2(\mathbf{r} \times \mathbf{n})]_x\,dS, \tag{20}$$

where **r** now specifies the position of the surface element $d\mathbf{S}$. Hence

$$\mathbf{\Gamma} = \oiint_S \varepsilon_o[(\mathbf{r} \times \mathbf{E})(\mathbf{E}\,.\,\mathbf{n}) - \tfrac{1}{2}E^2(\mathbf{r} \times \mathbf{n})]\,dS\,, \tag{21}$$

the corresponding result for two magnetic point poles being

$$\mathbf{\Gamma} = \oiint_S \mu_o[(\mathbf{r} \times \mathbf{H})(\mathbf{H}\,.\,\mathbf{n}) - \tfrac{1}{2}H^2(\mathbf{r} \times \mathbf{n})]\,dS\,. \tag{22}$$

2.2 The force on a pair of charges and the generalization to material bodies

If the single charge q_1 is replaced by a pair of separated charges, q_1' and q_1'', then it may readily be shown that the total force on the *pair* due to the presence of q_2 is again given by equation (15). Consider surfaces S, S' and S'' which enclose q_1' and q_1'' and also separate them as shown in Fig. 2.2

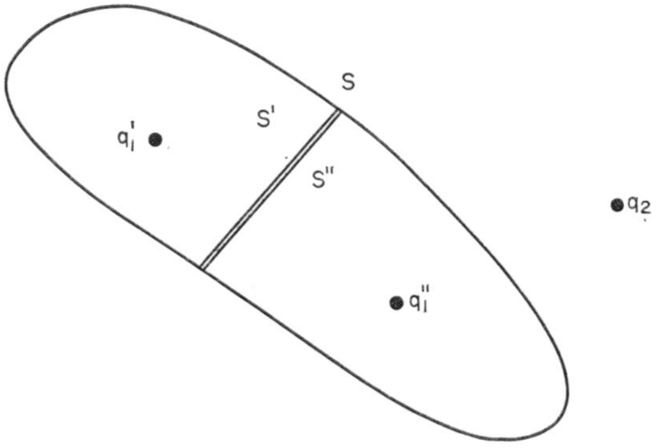

Fig. 2.2

The x-component of the force on q_1' due to the presence of q_2 is

$$F_x' = \oiint_{S'} \mathbf{U}\,.\,d\mathbf{S}\,, \tag{23}$$

whilst the x-component of the force on q_1'' due to the presence of q_2 is

$$F_x'' = \oint\!\!\oint_{S''} \mathbf{U} . d\mathbf{S} . \tag{24}$$

But these integrals are equal and opposite over the common surface ($d\mathbf{S}$ changes sign), so that

$$F_x' + F_x'' = \oint\!\!\oint_{S'} \mathbf{U} . d\mathbf{S} + \oint\!\!\oint_{S''} \mathbf{U} . d\mathbf{S} = \oint\!\!\oint_{S} \mathbf{U} . d\mathbf{S} , \tag{25}$$

with similar relations for the y- and z-components. Thus if q_1' and q_1'' are constrained to move together in some way the total force on the system is again given by (15). If equation (21) is used to obtain two equations, corresponding to (23) and (24), for the components of $\mathbf{\Gamma}$ associated with q_1' and q_1'' then it may be shown in the same way that the total torque $\mathbf{\Gamma}$ is again given by (21).

Although the results obtained above may be generalized to any number of individual charges—or poles in the magnetic analogue—it is not possible to pass over to the case of a material body by asserting that the body can be regarded as a very large number of charges or poles. If a macroscopic body is divided into smaller and smaller parts, it is only when the division reaches an atomic scale that the particle-like nature of matter becomes evident. At this point a description of the behaviour of matter in classical terms is not available and recourse must be had to quantum mechanics. However, all available experimental evidence indicates that the total ponderomotive force on a material body in a field is, in fact, given by (15) or (18) and that the total ponderomotive torque is given by (21) or (22). The method of calculating the total ponderomotive force by integrating a force distribution over a surface which encloses the body but is not necessarily coincident with it dates back to Maxwell (1873), and the system of forces acting on elements of the surface is usually referred to as the first Maxwell stress system.

For such a surface, equation (15) assumes a particularly simple form when the element $d\mathbf{S}$ is part of, or is perpendicular to, an equipotential surface. For an equipotential surface, $\mathbf{E} = E\mathbf{n}$ and

$$d\mathbf{F} = \tfrac{1}{2}\varepsilon_0 E^2 \mathbf{n}\, dS , \tag{26a}$$

whilst, for a surface element that is perpendicular to an equipotential surface, $(\mathbf{E} \cdot \mathbf{n}) = 0$ and

$$d\mathbf{F} = -\tfrac{1}{2}\varepsilon_o E^2 \mathbf{n}\, dS\dagger . \tag{26b}$$

Maxwell interpreted these forces in terms of the stresses in an elastic medium and so was led to the idea of electromagnetic forces being transmitted by stresses in an all-pervading 'ether'. From this point of view each tube of force is visualized as pulling on an equipotential surface with a normal force $\frac{1}{2}\varepsilon_o E^2$ per unit area, the tubes of force themselves being subjected to a longitudinal tension of magnitude

$$\frac{dF}{dS} = \tfrac{1}{2}\varepsilon_o E^2 \tag{27}$$

and a transverse pressure (inwards) of the same magnitude. Although these Maxwell stresses are now assumed to have no *physical* reality they do provide a convenient method of calculation, in which it is an obvious advantage to employ, whenever possible, surfaces of integration that are everywhere either parallel or perpendicular to the field, for it is then only necessary to take normal forces into account (the tangential ones being zero).

Because of the objections raised above to the derivation of equations (15), (18), (21) and (22) by generalizing the arguments of 2.1, a possible alternative method of derivation will be considered in subsequent sections. It should be noted that the discussion so far has not included any reference to the way in which the ponderomotive force is *distributed* within a material body. This is fundamental to the method of derivation used: for example, if the charges q_1' and q_1'' (of Fig. 2.2) are constrained to move together in some way, no information may be obtained on the force acting between q_1' and q_1'' by considering conditions only on the surface S. The mechanical stress in the constraining member is therefore unknown and the same conclusion may be drawn about stresses in material bodies. The problem of the specification of the distribution of the ponderomotive force within a material body in a field is considered in detail in Chapters 3 and 4.

2.3 Electromagnetic conditions within matter

(*a*) *The microscopic Maxwell's equations.* The fact that the force distribution was not specified by the analysis given above suggests

† It is not, of course, implied that $d\mathbf{F}$ is a force *acting* at the element dS.

that it might be desirable to look more closely at the specification of electromagnetic conditions within matter. As intimated in 1.6, the macroscopic field vectors **E** and **B** are related within material media to average values of the true electric field, denoted by **e**, and the true magnetic induction, denoted by **b**. It must be remembered that a material body is not a continuous structure but is made up of atoms or molecules separated by relatively large regions of intermolecular space. The fields **e** and **b** within the body therefore vary rapidly as functions of position. It is possible, however, to obtain space-average values of **e** and **b** by averaging over large regions containing many molecules. Since the molecules are also in motion it is also necessary to supplement this spatial average with a temporal average.

When a spatial averaging of a function $f(x, y, z, t)$ over a small volume τ centred on the point (x, y, z) is followed by a temporal averaging of $f(x, y, z, t)$ over a small time interval T centred on the time t, then the combined average will be denoted by $\bar{f}(x, y, z, t)$. Clearly,

$$\bar{f}(x, y, z, t) = \frac{1}{T\tau}\int_T\iiint_\tau f(x+\xi,\ y+\eta, z+\zeta,\ t+\theta)\,d\xi\,d\eta\,d\zeta\,d\theta\,, \tag{28}$$

where t is the origin of the coordinate θ that locates instants in the interval T, and (x, y, z) is the origin of the coordinates ξ, η, ζ that locate points in the volume τ. The average of a vector function is obtained by using (28) to average its three components, so that, for example,

$$\begin{aligned}\mathbf{E} = \bar{\mathbf{e}} &= \bar{\mathbf{e}}(x, y, z, t)\\ &= \frac{1}{T\tau}\int_T\iiint_\tau \mathbf{e}(x+\xi, y+\eta, z+\zeta, t+\theta)\,d\xi\,d\eta\,d\zeta\,d\theta\,,\end{aligned} \tag{29}$$

with a similar expression for $\mathbf{B} = \bar{\mathbf{b}}$. It may be noted that the volume τ contains a number of molecules so that, for example, $\bar{\mathbf{e}}$ is the average over a number of molecules and is not the field acting at a single molecule. It is therefore not the same as the effective local field acting on a molecule—a quantity that is introduced when the polarizability of a dielectric is under consideration.

It is a fundamental property of the averages defined by (28) that differentiation and averaging may be interchanged. To prove this it must be remembered that differentiation of an averaged quantity involves small displacements of the centres of the volume τ and the interval T without altering the range of values of the variables ξ, η, ζ and θ relative to these centres. Thus, for example,

$$\frac{\partial \bar{f}}{\partial x} = \frac{\partial}{\partial x}\left[\frac{1}{T\tau}\int\limits_T\iiint\limits_\tau f(x+\xi, y+\eta, z+\zeta, t+\theta)\, d\xi\, d\eta\, d\zeta\, d\theta\right]$$

$$= \frac{1}{T\tau}\int\limits_T\iiint\limits_\tau \frac{\partial}{\partial x} f(x+\xi, y+\eta, z+\zeta, t+\theta)\, d\xi\, d\eta\, d\zeta\, d\theta$$

$$= \frac{1}{T\tau}\int\limits_T\iiint\limits_\tau \frac{\partial}{\partial \xi} f(x+\xi, y+\eta, z+\zeta, t+\theta)\, d\xi\, d\eta\, d\zeta\, d\theta$$

$$= \overline{\frac{\partial f}{\partial x}}. \tag{30}$$

The linear operation of averaging may therefore be commuted with linear differential operators so that, for example,

$$\overline{\text{curl}\,\mathbf{e}} = \text{curl}\,\bar{\mathbf{e}}, \tag{31a}$$

and

$$\overline{\frac{\partial \mathbf{b}}{\partial t}} = \frac{\partial \bar{\mathbf{b}}}{\partial t}. \tag{31b}$$

Since, as discussed in 1.6, matter is essentially free space plus charge, the microscopic fields **e** and **b** must be subject to the free-space form of Maxwell's equations. However, although the macroscopic field vectors may be everywhere independent of time this will not be true of the microscopic quantities. Thus even for static macroscopic fields it is necessary to consider the time-dependent form of Maxwell's equations. The microscopic fields **e** and **b** therefore satisfy the equations

$$\text{curl}\,\mathbf{e} = -\frac{\partial \mathbf{h}}{\partial t}, \tag{32a}$$

$$\text{div}\,\mathbf{e} = \frac{\omega}{\varepsilon_o}, \tag{32b}$$

$$\text{curl}\,\mathbf{b} = \mu_o\left[\mathbf{j} + \varepsilon_o\frac{\partial \mathbf{e}}{\partial t}\right], \tag{32c}$$

$$\text{div}\,\mathbf{b} = 0, \tag{32d}$$

where the quantities ω and $\mathbf{j}$ are true microscopic charge and current densities that include both the extrinsic densities ρ and $\mathbf{J}$ and the contributions from the charges comprising the solid material. If both sides of these equations are averaged then equations (31) and similar relations obtained by commuting differentiation and averaging may be used to obtain the results

$$\text{curl}\,\bar{\mathbf{e}} = -\frac{\partial \bar{\mathbf{b}}}{\partial t}, \tag{33a}$$

$$\text{div}\,\bar{\mathbf{e}} = \bar{\omega}/\varepsilon_o, \tag{33b}$$

$$\text{curl}\,\bar{\mathbf{b}} = \mu_o\left[\bar{\mathbf{j}} + \varepsilon_o\frac{\partial \bar{\mathbf{e}}}{\partial t}\right], \tag{33c}$$

$$\text{div}\,\bar{\mathbf{b}} = 0. \tag{33d}$$

However $\mathbf{E} = \bar{\mathbf{e}}$ and $\mathbf{B} = \bar{\mathbf{b}}$, so that

$$\text{curl}\,\mathbf{E} = -\frac{\partial \mathbf{B}}{\partial t}, \tag{34a}$$

$$\text{div}\,\mathbf{E} = \bar{\omega}/\varepsilon_o, \tag{34b}$$

$$\text{curl}\,\mathbf{B} = \mu_o\left[\bar{\mathbf{j}} + \varepsilon_o\frac{\partial \mathbf{E}}{\partial t}\right], \tag{34c}$$

$$\text{div}\,\mathbf{B} = 0. \tag{34d}$$

Equations (34a) and (34d) are identical with the corresponding macroscopic Maxwell's equations: in order to determine whether the other two equations agree with Maxwell's equations it is necessary to evaluate the average charge density $\bar{\omega}$ and the average current density $\bar{\mathbf{j}}$.

(*b*) *The average charge and current densities*. Clearly, if the extrinsic charge density ρ is non-zero, this will be an important contribution to the average charge density $\bar{\omega}$, but it is by no means the only contribution. Consider, for example, an ionic dielectric—a familiar example being the compound sodium chloride—in a polarized but uncharged state. Since there are as many positive ions as negative ions it might be thought that in this case the average charge density would be given by $\bar{\omega} = \rho = 0$. However, this neglects a contribution due to non-uniformity of polarization, the existence of which may be demonstrated as follows. Imagine that the ions are true point charges and let the vector **R** represent the displacement of the positive ions with respect to the negative ions which, in this simple example, may be assumed to remain stationary. **R** is a macroscopic vector point function, in other words it is continuous and slowly varying on the atomic scale, although it has no physical significance in the regions between the ions. To calculate the average charge density in the polarized ionic dielectric, consider an element of volume $dV = dx\,dy\,dz$ containing many atoms and bounded by the planes x, $x + dx$, y, $y + dy$, z, $z + dz$. If ρ_o is the (macroscopic) average *positive* charge per unit volume (in the initial neutral distribution of charge) then the net charge entering dV through the two faces perpendicular to the x-axis is given by

$$[\rho_o R_x]\,dy\,dz - \left[\rho_o R_x + \frac{\partial}{\partial x}(\rho_o R_x)\,dx\right]dy\,dz = -\frac{\partial P_x}{\partial x}\,dV, \qquad (35)$$

where $\mathbf{P} = \rho_o \mathbf{R}$ may be identified as the macroscopic polarization. The net charge per unit volume produced by the polarization of the medium is therefore

$$-\left[\frac{\partial P_x}{\partial x} + \frac{\partial P_y}{\partial y} + \frac{\partial P_z}{\partial z}\right] = -\operatorname{div}\mathbf{P}, \qquad (36)$$

so that, in general,

$$\varpi = \rho - \operatorname{div} \mathbf{P}. \tag{37}$$

This result may also be obtained by observing that the charge lost to a volume V by crossing an element of surface $d\mathbf{S} = \mathbf{n}\, dS$ is $\rho_o \mathbf{R} \cdot d\mathbf{S} = \mathbf{P} \cdot \mathbf{n}\, dS$ and that, by the Gauss divergence theorem

$$\oiint_S - \mathbf{P} . \mathbf{n}\, dS = \iiint_V - \operatorname{div} \mathbf{P}\, dV. \tag{38}$$

Substitution of (37) in (34b) yields div $(\varepsilon_o \mathbf{E} + \mathbf{P}) = \rho$ which may be compared with the macroscopic Maxwell's equation div $\mathbf{D} = \rho$. Although the identification of $\mathbf{D}$ and $\varepsilon_o \mathbf{E} + \mathbf{P}$ is generally assumed to be valid for all types of dielectrics there is actually a further contribution to ϖ that arises because the ions (or molecules) may not, in fact, be treated as true point charges.

The calculation of this contribution may most conveniently be made by evaluating the charge transported across a surface element $d\mathbf{S}$ at the boundary of two adjacent volume elements. Let the position of each molecule be specified by a vector $\mathbf{r}'$ that locates some interior point P', whilst the position of any other point P'' of the molecule is specified by a vector $\mathbf{r}''$ that joins P' to P''. If the whole charge of each molecule were concentrated at some point (P') in the interior of the molecule then the average charge density would be zero, assuming that, as before, the dielectric is initially uncharged. The value of ϖ may therefore be calculated by considering the process in which these concentrated charges move back to restore the original charge distribution, and in particular by evaluating the amount of charge transported across $d\mathbf{S}$ in this process. Clearly, there is no contribution if P' is remote from dS, but if $\mathbf{r}''$ intersects dS there is a contribution $\omega(\mathbf{r}', \mathbf{r}'')\, d\tau'$ from each microscopic element of volume $d\tau'$ within the molecule. The microscopic charge density $\omega(\mathbf{r}', \mathbf{r}'')$ depends not only on $\mathbf{r}''$ but also on $\mathbf{r}'$ because the molecular charge distribution may be influenced by an external field varying slowly in space. The total charge transported across dS is obtained by summing such contributions both over the whole molecule and over all the molecules that are near enough to the element dS. To avoid unessential complications it will be assumed that all these molecules (which are subject to sensibly the same external influence) have the same orientation in space, that is they can be made to coincide by a simple translation.

If the summation is performed by first keeping $\mathbf{r}''$ fixed and summing over the separate molecules, the only molecules that contribute are those within a perpendicular distance $\mathbf{r}''.\mathbf{n}$ of dS, and the number of such molecules is $N(\mathbf{r}')\mathbf{r}''.\mathbf{n}\,dS$, where $N(\mathbf{r}')$ is the slowly-varying macroscopic number density of molecules. However, the vector $\mathbf{r}'$ is not constant for all the molecules within a perpendicular distance $\mathbf{r}''.\mathbf{n}$ of dS; it varies between $\mathbf{r}$ and $\mathbf{r}-\mathbf{r}''$, where the vector $\mathbf{r}$ specifies the position of the element dS. The contribution to the charge transported across dS obtained by summing with fixed $\mathbf{r}''$ is therefore

$$\int_{p=0}^{p=1}[\omega(\mathbf{r}-p\mathbf{r}'',\mathbf{r}'')\,d\tau' N(\mathbf{r}-p\mathbf{r}'')\mathbf{r}''.\mathbf{n}\,dS]\,dp$$

$$= d\tau'\,dS\mathbf{r}''.\mathbf{n}\int_{p=0}^{p=1}\omega(\mathbf{r}-p\mathbf{r}'',\mathbf{r}'')N(\mathbf{r}-p\mathbf{r}'')\,dp. \qquad (39)$$

The scalar function $\omega N = \omega(\mathbf{r}-p\mathbf{r}'',\mathbf{r}'')N(\mathbf{r}-p\mathbf{r}'')$, which varies slowly for fixed $\mathbf{r}''$, may be replaced by the first two terms of a Taylor expansion about the point $\mathbf{r}$, thus

$$\omega(\mathbf{r}-p\mathbf{r}'',\mathbf{r}'')N(\mathbf{r}-p\mathbf{r}'') = \omega(\mathbf{r},\mathbf{r}'')N(\mathbf{r}) - p\mathbf{r}''.\nabla_{\mathbf{r}}(\omega N), \qquad (40)$$

so that (39) becomes

$$d\tau'\,dS\mathbf{r}''.\mathbf{n}\int_{p=0}^{p=1}[\omega(\mathbf{r},\mathbf{r}'')N(\mathbf{r}) - p\mathbf{r}''.\nabla_{\mathbf{r}}(\omega N)]\,dp$$

$$= d\mathbf{S}.\mathbf{r}''[\omega(\mathbf{r},\mathbf{r}'')N(\mathbf{r}) - \tfrac{1}{2}\mathbf{r}''.\nabla_{\mathbf{r}}(\omega N)]\,d\tau'. \qquad (41)$$

This expression must now be integrated over τ', the volume of the molecule, to give, for the net charge crossing dS when the charge distribution in the molecules is restored,

$$dS\left\{\mathbf{n}\,.\iiint_{\tau'}\mathbf{r}''\omega(\mathbf{r},\mathbf{r}'')N(\mathbf{r}')\,d\tau' - \tfrac{1}{2}\mathbf{n}\,.\iiint_{\tau'}\mathbf{r}''[\mathbf{r}''\,.\,\nabla_{\mathbf{r}}(\omega N)]\,d\tau'\right\}$$

$$= dS\left\{n_x N\iiint_{\tau'} r''_x\omega\,d\tau' + n_y N\iiint_{\tau'} r''_y\omega\,d\tau' + n_z N\iiint_{\tau'} r''_z\omega\,dt'\right.$$

$$- \tfrac{1}{2}n_x\frac{\partial}{\partial x}N\iiint_{\tau'} r''_x r''_x\omega\,d\tau' - \tfrac{1}{2}n_x\frac{\partial}{\partial y}N\iiint_{\tau'} r''_x r''_y\omega\,d\tau'$$

$$- \tfrac{1}{2}n_x\frac{\partial}{\partial z}N\iiint_{\tau'} r''_x r''_z\omega\,d\tau'$$

$$- \tfrac{1}{2}n_y\frac{\partial}{\partial x}N\iiint_{\tau'} r''_y r''_x\omega\,d\tau' - \tfrac{1}{2}n_y\frac{\partial}{\partial y}N\iiint_{\tau'} r''_y r''_y\omega\,d\tau'$$

$$- \tfrac{1}{2}n_y\frac{\partial}{\partial z}N\iiint_{\tau'} r''_y r''_z\omega\,d\tau'$$

$$- \tfrac{1}{2}n_z\frac{\partial}{\partial x}N\iiint_{\tau'} r''_z r''_x\omega\,d\tau' - \tfrac{1}{2}n_z\frac{\partial}{\partial y}N\iiint_{\tau'} r''_z r''_y\omega\,dt'$$

$$\left.- \tfrac{1}{2}n_z\frac{\partial}{\partial z}N\iiint_{\tau'} r''_z r''_z\omega\,d\tau'\right\}. \qquad (42)$$

This equation involves the structure of the molecule through a series of quantities called the electrical multipole moments: there are three terms that are associated with the electric dipole moment

$$\mathbf{p} = \iiint_{v'}\mathbf{r}''\omega\,d\tau' \qquad (43)$$

and nine terms that are associated with the electrical quadrupole moment tensor **q**, the components of which have the form

$$q_{xx} = \tfrac{1}{2}\iiint_{\tau'} r''_x r''_x \omega \, d\tau' , \qquad q_{xy} = \tfrac{1}{2}\iiint_{\tau'} r''_x r''_y \omega \, d\tau' , \tag{44}$$

and so on. The successive multipole moments give an increasingly detailed picture of the charge distribution within the molecule, but in practice it is often sufficient to retain only the dipole term. If the last nine terms in equation (42) are represented by $-\tfrac{1}{2}\, dS\mathbf{n}\,.\,\mathrm{Div}\,(\mathbf{q}N)$, the symbol Div being one that is sometimes used when working with a dyadic notation, then the net charge crossing dS is

$$dS\mathbf{n}\,.\,[\mathbf{p}N - \mathrm{Div}\,(\mathbf{q}N)] = dS\mathbf{n}\,.\,[\mathbf{P} - \mathrm{Div}\,\mathbf{Q}] , \tag{45}$$

where the macroscopic dipole and quadrupole moments are given by $\mathbf{P} = N\mathbf{p}$ and $\mathbf{Q} = N\mathbf{q}$. However, the Gauss divergence theorem may then be used to show that

$$\oint\!\!\oint_S [\mathbf{P} - \mathrm{Div}\,\mathbf{Q}]\,.\,d\mathbf{S} = \iiint_V \mathrm{div}[\mathbf{P} - \mathrm{Div}\,\mathbf{Q}]\,dV \tag{46}$$

and hence that, in general,

$$\bar{\omega} = \rho - \mathrm{div}[\mathbf{P} - \mathrm{Div}\,\mathbf{Q}] . \tag{47}$$

Substitution of (47) in (34b) yields

$$\mathrm{div}[\varepsilon_o\mathbf{E} + \mathbf{P} - \mathrm{Div}\,\mathbf{Q}] = \rho , \tag{48}$$

and, on comparison with the macroscopic Maxwell's equation

$$\mathrm{div}\,\mathbf{D} = \rho , \tag{49}$$

the relationship

$$\mathbf{D} = \varepsilon_o\mathbf{E} + \mathbf{P} - \mathrm{Div}\,\mathbf{Q} , \tag{50}$$

which differs from the usual expression by the occurrence of the quadrupole term.

In a similar way (Problem 1) it can be shown that the average current density is given by

$$\bar{\mathbf{j}} = \mathbf{J} + \frac{\partial}{\partial t}[\mathbf{P} - \mathrm{Div}\,\mathbf{Q}] + \frac{1}{\mu_o}\,\mathrm{curl}\,\mathbf{I} , \tag{51}$$

where the magnetization

$$\mathbf{I} = \tfrac{1}{2}\mu_o N \iiint_{\tau'} \mathbf{r}'' \times \mathbf{j}\, d\tau' \tag{52}$$

is expressed in terms of a magnetic dipole moment. There are, of course, higher magnetic multipoles but if the electrical and magnetic cases are treated to the same degree of approximation there is always one less term in the latter. Substitution of (51) in (34c) gives

$$\operatorname{curl}\left[\frac{\mathbf{B} - \mathbf{I}}{\mu_o}\right] = \mathbf{J} + \frac{\partial}{\partial t}[\varepsilon_o \mathbf{E} + \mathbf{P} - \operatorname{Div} \mathbf{Q}] \tag{53a}$$

or

$$\operatorname{curl} \mathbf{H} = \mathbf{J} + \frac{\partial \mathbf{D}}{\partial t} \tag{53b}$$

where

$$\mathbf{B} = \mu_o \mathbf{H} + \mathbf{I} \tag{54}$$

and **D** is given by (50). It has therefore been shown that the relationships $\mathbf{E} = \bar{\mathbf{e}}$ and $\mathbf{B} = \bar{\mathbf{b}}$ are consistent with the usual macroscopic Maxwell's equations (34a), (49), (53b) and (34d). In addition, equations (50) and (54) that relate the polarization, **P**, and magnetization, **I**, to the electrical and magnetic field quantities agree with the corresponding equations in electromagnetic theory, although in the most well-known form of that theory the higher multipoles are neglected. The analogy between microscopic and macroscopic electromagnetic theory may be completed by establishing the connection between the microscopic and macroscopic potentials.

(*c*) *The scalar and vector potentials.* In 1.3 the static forms of Maxwell's equations were solved by obtaining expressions for scalar and vector potentials. A similar process can be carried out for equations (32) and this process is greatly facilitated by the existence of two mathematical theorems associated with the names of Helmholtz and Poisson. The Helmholtz theorem, which was discussed in 1.5, states that a vector **F** may be written in the form

$$\mathbf{F} = -\operatorname{grad} \Phi_F + \operatorname{curl} \mathbf{A}_F, \tag{55a}$$

where

$$\Phi_F = \frac{1}{4\pi}\iiint\limits_V \frac{\operatorname{div}\mathbf{F}}{r}\,dV, \tag{55b}$$

$$\mathbf{A}_F = \frac{1}{4\pi}\iiint\limits_V \frac{\operatorname{curl}\mathbf{F}}{r}\,dV. \tag{55c}$$

Since div $\mathbf{F} = -\Delta\Phi_F$, the scalar potential Φ_F satisfies the equation

$$\Phi_F = -\frac{1}{4\pi}\iiint\limits_V \frac{\Delta\Phi_F}{r}\,dV. \tag{56}$$

Poisson's theorem asserts that a similar relation holds for any well-behaved scalar function f (Problem 2), so that, in general,

$$f = -\frac{1}{4\pi}\iiint\limits_\infty \frac{\Delta f}{r}\,dV. \tag{57}$$

Applying this result to the three components of a vector $\mathbf{F}$ gives

$$\mathbf{F} = -\frac{1}{4\pi}\iiint\limits_\infty \frac{\Delta\mathbf{F}}{r}\,dV. \tag{58}$$

The application of Helmholtz's theorem to the microscopic Maxwell's equations (32) yields

$$\mathbf{e} = -\operatorname{grad}\phi_e + \operatorname{curl}\mathbf{a}_e, \tag{59a}$$

where

$$\phi_e = \frac{1}{4\pi}\iiint\limits_V \frac{\omega}{\varepsilon_o r}\,dV, \tag{59b}$$

$$\mathbf{a}_e = -\frac{1}{4\pi}\iiint\limits_V \frac{1}{r}\frac{\partial\mathbf{b}}{\partial t}\,dV \tag{59c}$$

and

$$\mathbf{b} = \operatorname{curl}\mathbf{a}_b, \tag{60a}$$

where

$$\mathbf{a}_b = \frac{\mu_o}{4\pi}\iiint\limits_V \left[\frac{\mathbf{j}}{r} + \frac{\varepsilon_o}{r}\frac{\partial \mathbf{e}}{\partial t}\right] dV. \tag{60b}$$

Since, however, curl $\mathbf{a}_e = -\partial \mathbf{a}_b/\partial t$, the electric and magnetic vectors may be expressed in terms of only ϕ_e and $\mathbf{a}_b$, thus

$$\mathbf{e} = -\text{grad}\, \phi_e - \frac{\partial \mathbf{a}_b}{\partial t}, \tag{61a}$$

$$\mathbf{b} = \text{curl}\, \mathbf{a}_b . \tag{61b}$$

As mentioned in 1.3 the vector potential is not uniquely defined by specifying its curl, for **b** is also equal to the curl of some vector **a** where

$$\mathbf{a} = \mathbf{a}_b - \text{grad}\, \psi, \tag{62}$$

and ψ is any arbitrary scalar function of position. The vector **b** is therefore unaltered by the subtraction of grad ψ from $\mathbf{a}_b$, and in order that **e** shall also be unaltered it is necessary to make a simultaneous addition of $\partial\psi/\partial t$ to the potential ϕ_e. Thus

$$\mathbf{e} = -\text{grad}\, \phi_e - \frac{\partial \mathbf{a}_b}{\partial t} = -\text{grad}\, \phi - \frac{\partial \mathbf{a}}{\partial t}, \tag{63a}$$

$$\mathbf{b} = \text{curl}\, \mathbf{a}_b = \text{curl}\, \mathbf{a}, \tag{63b}$$

where

$$\phi = \phi_e + \frac{\partial \psi}{\partial t}, \tag{64a}$$

$$\mathbf{a} = \mathbf{a}_b - \text{grad}\, \psi . \tag{64b}$$

An infinite number of pairs of potentials, ϕ and **a**, can be constructed by altering the function ψ and these all give the same fields **e** and **b**. One such pair is, however, of special significance, for substitution of (63a) and (63b) into (32b) and (32c) gives

$$\Delta\phi + \text{div}\frac{\partial \mathbf{a}}{\partial t} = -\omega/\varepsilon_o, \tag{65a}$$

$$\text{curl curl}\, \mathbf{a} \equiv \text{grad div}\, \mathbf{a} - \Delta \mathbf{a} = \mu_o \mathbf{j} - \varepsilon_o\mu_o\, \text{grad}\frac{\partial \phi}{\partial t} - \varepsilon_o\mu_o \frac{\partial \mathbf{a}}{\partial t}, \tag{65b}$$

and the imposition upon ϕ and **a** of the subsidiary condition

$$\operatorname{div} \mathbf{a} + \varepsilon_o \mu_o \frac{\partial \phi}{\partial t} = 0 \tag{66}$$

permits the separation of equations (65a) and (65b) into one equation that involves ϕ only and another that involves **a** only. The condition (66) is known as the Lorentz condition and for it to be satisfied it is merely necessary that the function ψ satisfies the equation

$$\Delta \psi - \varepsilon_o \mu_o \frac{\partial^2 \psi}{\partial t^2} = \operatorname{div} \mathbf{a}_b + \varepsilon_o \mu_o \frac{\partial \phi_e}{\partial t} . \tag{67}$$

When the Lorentz condition is imposed equations (65) reduce to the form

$$\Delta \phi - \frac{1}{c^2} \frac{\partial^2 \phi}{\partial t^2} = -\omega / \varepsilon_o , \tag{68a}$$

$$\Delta \mathbf{a} - \frac{1}{c^2} \frac{\partial^2 \mathbf{a}}{\partial t^2} = -\mu_o \mathbf{j} , \tag{68b}$$

where $c = (\varepsilon_o \mu_o)^{-1/2}$ is the velocity of light in free space. If the symbolic operator $\Box$, known as the D'Alembertian and defined by

$$\Box = \Delta - \frac{1}{c^2} \frac{\partial^2}{\partial t^2} , \tag{69}$$

is introduced, it may be seen that ϕ and **a** satisfy the equations

$$\Box \phi = -\omega / \varepsilon_o , \tag{70a}$$

$$\Box \mathbf{a} = -\mu_o \mathbf{j} . \tag{70b}$$

In summary, therefore, **e** and **b** are given by

$$\mathbf{e} = -\operatorname{grad} \phi - \frac{\partial \mathbf{a}}{\partial t} , \tag{71a}$$

$$\mathbf{b} = \operatorname{curl} \mathbf{a} , \tag{71b}$$

where the potentials

$$\phi = \frac{1}{4\pi}\iiint\limits_V \frac{\omega}{\varepsilon_o r}\,dV + \frac{\partial\psi}{\partial t}, \tag{72a}$$

$$\mathbf{a} = \frac{\mu_o}{4\pi}\iiint\limits_V \left[\frac{\mathbf{j}}{r} + \frac{\varepsilon_o}{r}\frac{\partial \mathbf{e}}{\partial t}\right] dV - \operatorname{grad}\psi, \tag{72b}$$

satisfy the Lorentz condition and the equations

$$\Box\phi = -\omega/\varepsilon_o, \tag{73a}$$

$$\Box\mathbf{a} = -\mu_o\mathbf{j}. \tag{73b}$$

Equations (71) are not completely general solutions of equations (32), for to them may be added any particular solution of the *homogeneous* equations obtained by putting $\omega = 0 = \mathbf{j}$ in (32). Solutions of the form (71) have already been allowed for but, from the symmetry of the homogeneous equations, there are obviously possible solutions of the form

$$\mathbf{e} = -\frac{1}{\varepsilon_o}\operatorname{curl}\mathbf{a}^*, \tag{74a}$$

$$\mathbf{b} = -\mu_o\left[\operatorname{grad}\phi^* - \frac{\partial\mathbf{a}^*}{\partial t}\right], \tag{74b}$$

where ϕ^* and $\mathbf{a}^*$ are subject only to the conditions

$$\Box\phi^* = 0 = \Box\mathbf{a}^*, \tag{75a}$$

$$\operatorname{div}\mathbf{a}^* + \varepsilon_o\mu_o\frac{\partial\phi^*}{\partial t} = 0. \tag{75b}$$

The functions ϕ^* and $\mathbf{a}^*$ are the potentials of source distributions that are entirely external to the region considered and in order to exclude such potentials from consideration it is usual to extend the integration over V to infinity and therefore to replace equations (72) by

$$\phi = \frac{1}{4\pi}\iiint\limits_{\infty}\frac{\omega}{\varepsilon_o r}\,dV + \frac{\partial\psi}{\partial t}, \tag{76a}$$

$$\mathbf{a} = \frac{\mu_o}{4\pi}\iiint\limits_{\infty}\left[\frac{\mathbf{j}}{r} + \frac{\varepsilon_o}{r}\frac{\partial\mathbf{e}}{\partial t}\right]dV - \operatorname{grad}\psi\,. \tag{76b}$$

Now these formulae for the potentials are of limited value, not only because of the occurrence of the function ψ but also because of the presence of the term involving $\partial\mathbf{e}/\partial t$. The physical origin of the unsatisfactory nature of these formulae lies in the fact that they attempt to relate the potentials to the simultaneous values of other electromagnetic quantities at a finite distance r from the point at which the potentials are evaluated. This situation can be rectified for although

$$\Box\phi = -\omega/\varepsilon_o \neq \Delta\phi\,, \tag{77a}$$

$$\Box\mathbf{a} = -\mu_o\mathbf{j} \neq \Delta\mathbf{a}\,, \tag{77b}$$

it may be shown that for any well-behaved scalar function f (Problem 3),

$$\iiint\limits_{\infty}\frac{[\Box f]_{\text{ret}}}{r}\,dV = \iiint\limits_{\infty}\frac{\Delta[f]_{\text{ret}}}{r}\,dV \tag{78}$$

where the symbol $[\;]_{\text{ret}}$ indicates that the quantity within should be evaluated not at time t but at the retarded time $t - r/c$. Thus, when Poisson's theorem is modified to allow for the retardation,

$$\phi = -\frac{1}{4\pi}\iiint\limits_{\infty}\frac{\Delta[\phi]_{\text{ret}}}{r}\,dV, \tag{79a}$$

$$\mathbf{a} = -\frac{1}{4\pi}\iiint\limits_{\infty}\frac{\Delta[\mathbf{a}]_{\text{ret}}}{r}\,dV, \tag{79b}$$

and equation (78) may be used to express the potentials in the form

$$\phi = -\frac{1}{4\pi}\iiint\limits_{\infty}\frac{[\Box\phi]_{ret}}{r}\,dV = \frac{1}{4\pi}\iiint\limits_{\infty}\frac{[\rho]_{ret}}{\varepsilon_o r}\,dV, \tag{80a}$$

$$\mathbf{a} = -\frac{1}{4\pi}\iiint\limits_{\infty}\frac{[\Box\mathbf{a}]_{ret}}{r}\,dV = \frac{1}{4\pi}\iiint\limits_{\infty}\frac{\mu_o[\mathbf{j}]_{ret}}{r}\,dV. \tag{80b}$$

These functions are known as retarded potentials. It is also possible to express ϕ and $\mathbf{a}$ in terms of advanced potentials but the customary formulation is the one given above, in which the potentials correspond to waves radiating away from charges rather than converging towards them. It may be noted that the above discussion has some relevance to the unsatisfactory way in which Maxwell's displacement current, $\varepsilon_o\partial\mathbf{e}/\partial t$, is often introduced into electromagnetism. In calculating the vector potential $\mathbf{a}$, it is possible to proceed from equation (72b) taking into account both the conduction current $\mathbf{j}$ and the displacement current $\varepsilon_o\partial\mathbf{e}/\partial t$ and assuming, by implication, that the electromagnetic action takes place instantaneously. The above reasoning shows, however, that it is also possible to use the retarded formula (80b) taking account only of conduction currents and supposing that the electromagnetic action is propagated with the velocity of light.

In order to relate ϕ and $\mathbf{a}$ to the macroscopic potentials Φ and $\mathbf{A}$ introduced in 1.2, the unretarded formulae (72) may be averaged with the aid of (47) and (51) to give

$$\bar{\phi} = \frac{1}{4\pi}\iiint\limits_{V}\frac{\operatorname{div}\mathbf{E}}{r}\,dV + \frac{\partial\Psi}{\partial t}, \tag{81a}$$

$$\bar{\mathbf{a}} = \frac{1}{4\pi}\iiint\limits_{V}\frac{\operatorname{curl}\mathbf{B}}{r}\,dV - \operatorname{grad}\Psi, \tag{81b}$$

where $\Psi = \bar{\psi}$. But these are just the scalar and vector potentials of macroscopic electromagnetic theory (Jackson 1962, Van Vleck 1932), for the case in which material bodies are present and ρ and $\mathbf{J}$ are not necessarily zero.

(*d*) *The total ponderomotive force.* The instantaneous force, $\zeta\, d\tau$, on an element of volume $d\tau$ of a material body depends on the microscopic field vectors **e** and **b**: in fact, the instantaneous force on the element $d\tau$ is

$$\zeta\, d\tau = (\omega \mathbf{e} + \mathbf{j} \times \mathbf{b})\, d\tau. \tag{82}$$

By using equations (32b) and (32c), the instantaneous force per unit volume may be written in the form

$$\zeta = (\omega \mathbf{e} + \mathbf{j} \times \mathbf{b}) = \varepsilon_o \mathbf{e} \operatorname{div} \mathbf{e} + \left[\frac{1}{\mu_o} \operatorname{curl} \mathbf{b} - \varepsilon_o \frac{\partial \mathbf{e}}{\partial t}\right] \times \mathbf{b}. \tag{83}$$

Moreover, this expression will be unaltered by adding any vector multiplied by div **b** or by adding the vector product of any vector with (curl **e** + $\partial \mathbf{b}/\partial t$), so that,

$$\begin{aligned}
\mathbf{f} &= (\omega \mathbf{e} + \mathbf{j} \times \mathbf{b}) \\
&= \varepsilon_o \mathbf{e} \operatorname{div} \mathbf{e} - \varepsilon_o \left[\mathbf{e} \times \operatorname{curl} \mathbf{e} + \mathbf{e} \times \frac{\partial \mathbf{b}}{\partial t}\right] \\
&\quad + \frac{1}{\mu_o} \mathbf{b} \operatorname{div} \mathbf{b} - \mathbf{b} \times \left[\frac{1}{\mu_o} \operatorname{curl} \mathbf{b} - \varepsilon_o \frac{\partial \mathbf{e}}{\partial t}\right] \\
&= \varepsilon_o [\mathbf{e} \operatorname{div} \mathbf{e} - \mathbf{e} \times \operatorname{curl} \mathbf{e}] \\
&\quad + \frac{1}{\mu_o} [\mathbf{b} \operatorname{div} \mathbf{b} - \mathbf{b} \times \operatorname{curl} \mathbf{b}] + \varepsilon_o \left[\mathbf{b} \times \frac{\partial \mathbf{e}}{\partial t} - \mathbf{e} \times \frac{\partial \mathbf{b}}{\partial t}\right].
\end{aligned} \tag{84}$$

Now the last term in (84) is just $\varepsilon_o \partial(\mathbf{b} \times \mathbf{e})/\partial t$ and when ζ is averaged according to (28) the contribution of this term to the average force density will be

$$\overline{\varepsilon_o \frac{\partial}{\partial t}(\mathbf{b} \times \mathbf{e})} = \varepsilon_o \frac{\partial}{\partial t}\overline{(\mathbf{b} \times \mathbf{e})}, \tag{85}$$

since the operations of time differentiation and averaging may be commuted. However, the problem under consideration is a static one, so that this contribution to $\bar{\zeta}$ can only be either zero or constant. A constant value would imply a continual increase (or decrease) in $\overline{(\mathbf{b} \times \mathbf{e})}$, but this is inconsistent with the fact that $\bar{\mathbf{b}} = \mathbf{B}$ and $\bar{\mathbf{e}} = \mathbf{E}$ are known to have finite values. It may therefore be concluded that the contribution of the last term in (84) to the average force density is zero and that

$$\bar{\zeta} = \varepsilon_o \overline{[\mathbf{e} \operatorname{div} \mathbf{e} - \mathbf{e} \times \operatorname{curl} \mathbf{e}]} + \frac{1}{\mu_o}\overline{[\mathbf{b} \operatorname{div} \mathbf{b} - \mathbf{b} \times \operatorname{curl} \mathbf{b}]}. \tag{86}$$

The corresponding total ponderomotive force is therefore

$$\mathbf{F} = \iiint_V \bar{\zeta}\, d\tau = \mathbf{F}^e + \mathbf{F}^m, \tag{87a}$$

where

$$\mathbf{F}^e = \iiint_V \varepsilon_o \overline{[\mathbf{e} \operatorname{div} \mathbf{e} - \mathbf{e} \times \operatorname{curl} \mathbf{e}]}\, d\tau, \tag{87b}$$

$$\mathbf{F}^m = \iiint_V \frac{1}{\mu_o} \overline{[\mathbf{b} \operatorname{div} \mathbf{b} - \mathbf{b} \times \operatorname{curl} \mathbf{b}]}\, d\tau. \tag{87c}$$

From the meaning of the averaging process defined by (28), it is immaterial whether the integration over τ is performed on an averaged function or on the original function after it has been subject only to averaging over the time interval T. It is therefore of interest to consider, for example, the integral

$$\mathbf{G}^e = \iiint_V \varepsilon_o [\mathbf{e} \operatorname{div} \mathbf{e} - \mathbf{e} \times \operatorname{curl} \mathbf{e}]\, d\tau, \tag{88}$$

of which $\mathbf{F}^e$ is the time average. Although $\mathbf{G}^e$ involves the microscopic electric field $\mathbf{e}$, which fluctuates rapidly within the body, it is possible to remove this complicating feature by transforming the volume integral into a surface integral. Since the microscopic vector **e**—unlike the macroscopic vector **E**—is continuous even through the surface of the material body, the surface of integration, S', may be chosen to be wholly outside the body. This is an attractive procedure, for at points outside the body there is no ambiguity about electrical conditions: **e** has the time-independent value $\mathbf{e} = \bar{\mathbf{e}} = \mathbf{E}$ and a formulation in terms of an integral over S' thus obviates any difficulties arising from the complexity of the composition of matter.

The transformation into a surface integral may be readily accomplished by considering the x-component of the integrand, for this is

$$\varepsilon_o[\mathbf{e}\,\mathrm{div}\,\mathbf{e} - \mathbf{e}\times\mathrm{curl}\,\mathbf{e}]_x = \varepsilon_o\left[e_x\frac{\partial e_x}{\partial x} + e_x\frac{\partial e_y}{\partial y} + e_x\frac{\partial e_z}{\partial z}\right]$$
$$- \varepsilon_o\left[e_y\frac{\partial e_y}{\partial x} - e_y\frac{\partial e_x}{\partial y} + e_z\frac{\partial e_z}{\partial x} - e_z\frac{\partial e_x}{\partial z}\right]$$
$$= \varepsilon_o\left[\frac{\partial}{\partial x}(e_x^2 - \tfrac{1}{2}e^2) + \frac{\partial}{\partial y}(e_x e_y) + \frac{\partial}{\partial z}(e_x e_z)\right] \tag{89}$$

and the corollary of the Gauss divergence theorem given by equation (17) may be used to express G_x^e in the form

$$G_x^e = \oint\!\!\oint_{S'} \varepsilon_o[\mathbf{e}(\mathbf{e}\,.\,\mathbf{n}) - \tfrac{1}{2}e^2\mathbf{n}]_x\,dS. \tag{90}$$

The other two components of $\mathbf{G}^e$ are given by similar expressions and, since S' is external to the body, **e** may be replaced by **E** to give

$$\mathbf{G}^e = \oint\!\!\oint_{S'} \varepsilon_o[\mathbf{E}(\mathbf{E}\,.\,\mathbf{n}) - \tfrac{1}{2}E^2\mathbf{n}]\,dS. \tag{91}$$

Now, the electrical ponderomotive force $\mathbf{F}^e$ is just the time average of $\mathbf{G}^e$, but from (91) $\mathbf{G}^e$ is itself independent of time, so that

$$\mathbf{F}^e = \oint\!\!\oint_{S'} \varepsilon_o[\mathbf{E}(\mathbf{E}\,.\,\mathbf{n}) - \tfrac{1}{2}E^2\mathbf{n}]\,dS, \tag{92}$$

which is identical with equation (15) of 2.1. By an entirely similar procedure, it may be shown that $\mathbf{F}^m$ is given by an analagous expression obtained by replacing ε_o and $\mathbf{E}$ by $1/\mu_o$ and $\mathbf{B}$ respectively in (92), and the resulting equation is identical with (18). When there is no externally applied electric field, then $\mathbf{e} = \mathbf{E}$ is zero everywhere outside the body and $\mathbf{F}^e$ vanishes. Similarly $\mathbf{F}^m$ vanishes when there is no applied magnetic field and it is therefore possible to separate the total ponderomotive force $\mathbf{F}$ into an electrical part $\mathbf{F}^e$ appropriate to zero applied magnetic field and a magnetic part $\mathbf{F}^m$ appropriate to zero applied electric field.

(*e*) *The total ponderomotive torque*. If the position of the volume element $d\tau$ is specified by the vector $\mathbf{r}$, the instantaneous torque about the origin of $\mathbf{r}$ due to $d\tau$ is given, per unit volume, by the expression

$$\mathbf{r} \times \boldsymbol{\zeta} = \mathbf{r} \times (\omega\mathbf{e} + \mathbf{j} \times \mathbf{b}) = \mathbf{r} \times \varepsilon_o[\mathbf{e}\,\mathrm{div}\,\mathbf{e} - \mathbf{e} \times \mathrm{curl}\,\mathbf{e}]$$
$$+ \mathbf{r} \times \frac{1}{\mu_o}[\mathbf{b}\,\mathrm{div}\,\mathbf{b} - \mathbf{b} \times \mathrm{curl}\,\mathbf{b}] + \mathbf{r} \times \varepsilon_o \frac{\partial}{\partial t}(\mathbf{b} \times \mathbf{e}). \quad (93)$$

Again, the last term can be ignored since it can not contribute, for static macroscopic fields, to the average torque per unit volume $\overline{(\mathbf{r} \times \boldsymbol{\zeta})}$. In obtaining the total ponderomotive torque $\boldsymbol{\Gamma}$ from $\overline{(\mathbf{r} \times \boldsymbol{\zeta})}$ the order of integration and spatial averaging is interchangeable, as in equation (87), so that

$$\boldsymbol{\Gamma} = \iiint_V \overline{(\mathbf{r} \times \boldsymbol{\zeta})}\, d\tau = \boldsymbol{\Gamma}^e + \boldsymbol{\Gamma}^m, \quad (94)$$

where $\boldsymbol{\Gamma}^e$ is the time average of the integral

$$\boldsymbol{\Delta}^e = \iiint_V \mathbf{r} \times \varepsilon_o[\mathbf{e}\,\mathrm{div}\,\mathbf{e} - \mathbf{e} \times \mathrm{curl}\,\mathbf{e}]\, d\tau \quad (95)$$

and $\boldsymbol{\Gamma}^m$ is the time average of a similar integral obtained by replacing ε_o and $\mathbf{e}$ by $1/\mu_o$ and $\mathbf{b}$ respectively.

Equation (95) may also be transformed into a surface integral over a surface S' that encloses the body, for the x-component of the integral is given by

$$\Delta_x^e = \iiint_V \varepsilon_o \Big\{ y\Big[e_z\frac{\partial e_x}{\partial x} + e_z\frac{\partial e_y}{\partial y} + e_z\frac{\partial e_z}{\partial z} + e_x\frac{\partial e_z}{\partial x} + e_y\frac{\partial e_z}{\partial y} - e_x\frac{\partial e_x}{\partial z} - e_y\frac{\partial e_y}{\partial z}\Big]$$

$$- z\Big[e_y\frac{\partial e_x}{\partial x} + e_y\frac{\partial e_y}{\partial y} + e_y\frac{\partial e_z}{\partial z} + e_x\frac{\partial e_y}{\partial x} + e_z\frac{\partial e_y}{\partial z} - e_x\frac{\partial e_x}{\partial y} - e_z\frac{\partial e_z}{\partial y}\Big]\Big\} d\tau$$

$$= \iiint_V \varepsilon_o \Big\{ \frac{\partial}{\partial x}[e_x(ye_z - ze_y)] + \frac{\partial}{\partial y}[ye_ye_z - \tfrac{1}{2}z(2e_y^2 - e^2)] - \frac{\partial}{\partial z}[ze_ye_z - \tfrac{1}{2}y(2e_z^2 - e^2)]\Big\} d\tau \qquad (96)$$

and the corollary of the Gauss divergence theorem given by equation (17) may be used to express (96) in the form

$$\Delta_x^e = \oiint_{S'} \varepsilon_o[(ye_z - ze_y)e_xn_x + (ye_ye_z - ze_y^2)n_y + \tfrac{1}{2}ze^2n_y - (ze_ye_z - ye_z^2)n_z - \tfrac{1}{2}ye^2n_z]\, dS$$

$$= \oiint_{S'} \varepsilon_o[(ye_z - ze_y)(e_xn_x + e_yn_y + e_zn_z) - \tfrac{1}{2}e^2(yn_z - zn_y)]\, dS$$

$$= \oiint_{S'} \varepsilon_o[(\mathbf{r} \times \mathbf{e})(\mathbf{e}\,.\,\mathbf{n}) - \tfrac{1}{2}e^2(\mathbf{r} \times \mathbf{n})]_x\, dS. \qquad (97)$$

The other two components of $\boldsymbol{\Delta}^e$ are given by similar expressions and, since S' is external to the body, $\mathbf{e} = \mathbf{E}$ everywhere on S'. It is therefore possible to substitute $\mathbf{E}$ for $\mathbf{e}$ to give a time-independent equation for $\boldsymbol{\Delta}^e$, so that both $\boldsymbol{\Gamma}^e$ and $\boldsymbol{\Delta}^e$ are given by the same expression, namely

$$\mathbf{\Gamma}^e = \oiint_{S'} \varepsilon_o[(\mathbf{r} \times \mathbf{E})(\mathbf{E}\,.\,\mathbf{n}) - \tfrac{1}{2}E^2(\mathbf{r} \times \mathbf{n})]\,dS, \tag{98}$$

which is identical with (21) of 2.1. The corresponding expression for the magnetic ponderomotive torque $\mathbf{\Gamma}^m$ is obtained by replacing ε_o and $\mathbf{E}$ with $1/\mu_o$ and $\mathbf{B}$ respectively in (98): the resulting equation is identical with (22).

(*f*) *Discussion.* In the present section (2.3) the expressions obtained in 2.1 and 2.2 for the total ponderomotive force and torque are derived by considering the specification of electromagnetic conditions within matter on a microscopic, or molecular, scale. The method is based on the Lorentz picture of matter as consisting of charges in motion in free space and on the validity of Maxwell's equations (32) at the microscopic level. Thus it is assumed, first, that it is possible to take a volume element $d\tau'$ small enough to specify the distribution of charge on a sub-molecular scale by means of a continuous density function ω (not to be confused with the slowly-varying macroscopic number density N) and, secondly, that whatever other restrictions may be imposed on the element of charge $\omega\, d\tau'$ it must conform to a microscopic formulation of electromagnetism appropriate to the motion of charge in free space. There is, of course, no direct way of verifying the truth of these assumptions but it has been shown that they lead, after suitable averaging, to the classical macroscopic formulation of electromagnetic theory. Furthermore, they yield expressions for the total ponderomotive force and torque which correspond to the first stress system of Maxwell and which are in agreement with all the available experimental evidence. However, there is a further implication—not so far verified by experiment—that the *distribution* of force within a material body is specified by equation (86) for $\bar{\zeta}$. This implication will not be pursued further here but it is relevant to the discussion of the distribution of ponderomotive force that is presented in Chapters 3 and 4.

It has already been pointed out that the microscopic vectors **e** and **b**—unlike their macroscopic counterparts—possess the advantage that they are continuous even on passing through the surface of the material body. However, there is another assumption that has been made implicitly in this section, namely the assumption that the material is isotropic. In reality most materials are not truly isotropic, they are polycrystalline and consist of an aggregate of small crystalline grains orientated at random. If the individual grains are small compared with the distances over which measurements of electrical and magnetic quantities are made, then the polycrystalline nature of the material does not, in practice, make any difference and the formulation of classical electromagnetism is appropriate. If the grains are small but not orientated at random then the methods of this section are inappropriate and to allow for this directionality in the material, macroscopic electromagnetic theory must be modified by making the permittivity, ε, and permeability, μ, tensors rather than scalars. In ferroelectric and ferromagnetic materials there is a further complication that the material may be divided into a number of domains, or regions that are polarized or magnetized to a fixed (saturation) value in a direction that is not, in general, coincident with that of the bulk (unsaturated) polarization or magnetization. However, in polycrystalline materials the domain structure is sufficiently broken up by the existence of the individual crystalline grains for the methods of this section to be appropriate provided that electromagnetic conditions are not investigated on a scale comparable with the size of the grains. It may therefore be concluded that the assumption of isotropy is also reasonable for polycrystalline materials provided the individual crystalline grains are small and orientated substantially at random.

2.4 Equivalent force systems

In the preceding section expressions were obtained for the total ponderomotive force, $\mathbf{F}$, and torque, $\mathbf{\Gamma}$, on a material body in terms of surface integrals. In addition, however, $\mathbf{F}$ and $\mathbf{\Gamma}$ may each be expressed as a sum of a surface and a volume integral, and the corresponding integrands then define an equivalent force system, or more exactly an equivalent system of surface stresses and force densities. Such systems are usually discussed in relation to magnetic rather than dielectric materials, presumably because of the familiarity of representing a long cylindrical magnet by means either of a surface distribution of magnetic poles at each end of the magnet or of circumferential electric currents flowing around the surface of the cylinder. In such a representation, a magnetic body is imagined to be replaced by a model consisting of a distribution of poles or currents (or both) disposed in such a way that the total magnetic field is indistinguishable from that existing at all points external to the body prior to its removal. The total ponderomotive force and torque on the model are then the same as those on the body, as may be seen by considering the equal and opposite action and reaction between the body and whatever external arrangement is the source of the field in which the body was originally placed. To use such models to deduce equivalent force systems it is necessary to know what field is produced by the model, not only at exterior points but also at points within the model.

For static fields curl **E** and div **B** are both zero so that Helmholtz's theorem may be used to express the macroscopic vectors **E** and **B** in the forms

$$\mathbf{E} = -\operatorname{grad} \frac{1}{4\pi} \iiint\limits_V \frac{\operatorname{div} \mathbf{E}}{r}\, dV, \tag{99a}$$

$$\mathbf{B} = \operatorname{curl} \frac{1}{4\pi} \iiint\limits_V \frac{\operatorname{curl} \mathbf{B}}{r}\, dV. \tag{99b}$$

Now although the vectors **E** and **B** are continuous inside and outside the body they do undergo discontinuities at the surface, S, of the material body. In using Helmholtz's theorem, allowance must therefore be made for this fact by including the contribution to the divergence and the curl arising from these discontinuities at the surface. The contribution to the divergence may be evaluated by enclosing S in a thin transitional layer. If $\mathbf{n}_1$ and $\mathbf{n}_2$ are normals drawn outwards from this layer (so that $\mathbf{n}_1$ is directed into the body), an application of the Gauss divergence theorem to a small portion of the layer shows that div **E** dV must be supplemented by

$$(\mathbf{E}_1 . \mathbf{n}_1 + \mathbf{E}_2 . \mathbf{n}_2)\, dS = (\mathbf{E}_2 - \mathbf{E}_1) . \mathbf{n} = (\mathbf{E}' - \mathbf{E}) . \mathbf{n}, \tag{100}$$

where the prime is used, for clarity, to distinguish the field, $\mathbf{E}'(= \mathbf{E}_2)$, outside the surface S from the field $\mathbf{E}(= \mathbf{E}_1)$ inside. Similarly a corollary of the Gauss divergence theorem, namely

$$\iiint\limits_V \operatorname{curl} \mathbf{U}\, dV = \oint\!\!\oint\limits_S \mathbf{n} \times \mathbf{U}\, dS, \tag{101}$$

may be used to show that curl **B** dV must be supplemented by

$$(\mathbf{n}_1 \times \mathbf{B}_1 + \mathbf{n}_2 \times \mathbf{B}_2)\, dS = \mathbf{n} \times (\mathbf{B}' - \mathbf{B})\, dS . \tag{102}$$

The correct forms of equations (99) are therefore

$$\mathbf{E} = -\operatorname{grad} \Phi , \tag{103a}$$

$$\mathbf{B} = \operatorname{curl} \mathbf{A} , \tag{103b}$$

where

$$\Phi = \iiint\limits_V \frac{\operatorname{div} \mathbf{E}}{4\pi r}\, dV + \oiint\limits_S \frac{(\mathbf{E}' - \mathbf{E}) \,.\, \mathbf{n}}{4\pi r}\, dS , \tag{103c}$$

$$\mathbf{A} = \iiint\limits_V \frac{\operatorname{curl} \mathbf{B}}{4\pi r}\, dV + \oiint\limits_S \frac{\mathbf{n} \times (\mathbf{B}' - \mathbf{B})}{4\pi r}\, dS . \tag{103d}$$

However, neglecting quadrupole and higher moments, $\mathbf{E} = (\mathbf{D} - \mathbf{P})/\varepsilon_o$ and $\mathbf{B} = \mu_o \mathbf{H} + \mathbf{I}$, so that

$$\Phi = \iiint\limits_V \frac{\operatorname{div} \mathbf{D}}{4\pi\varepsilon_o r}\, dV + \iiint\limits_V \frac{-\operatorname{div} \mathbf{P}}{4\pi\varepsilon_o r}\, dV + \oiint\limits_S \frac{(\mathbf{D}' - \mathbf{D}) \,.\, \mathbf{n} + \mathbf{P} \,.\, \mathbf{n}}{4\pi\varepsilon_o r}\, dS , \tag{104a}$$

$$\mathbf{A} = \iiint\limits_V \frac{\mu_o \operatorname{curl} \mathbf{H}}{4\pi r}\, dV + \iiint\limits_V \frac{\operatorname{curl} \mathbf{I}}{4\pi r}\, dV + \oiint\limits_S \frac{\mathbf{n} \times \mu_o (\mathbf{H}' - \mathbf{H}) + \mathbf{I} \times \mathbf{n}}{4\pi r}\, dS . \tag{104b}$$

Furthermore, from the usual boundary conditions at the surface of the body, $(\mathbf{D}' - \mathbf{D}) \,.\, \mathbf{n} = \kappa$ and $\mathbf{n} \times (\mathbf{H}' - \mathbf{H}) = \mathbf{K}$, where κ is the extrinsic surface charge density and **K** the extrinsic surface current density. Thus, using (49) and (53b),

$$\Phi = \iiint\limits_V \frac{\rho + \rho^*}{4\pi\varepsilon_o r}\, dV + \oiint\limits_S \frac{\kappa + \kappa^*}{4\pi\varepsilon_o r}\, dS , \tag{105a}$$

$$\mathbf{A} = \iiint\limits_V \frac{\mu_o (\mathbf{J} + \mathbf{J}^*)}{4\pi r}\, dV + \oiint\limits_S \frac{\mu_o (\mathbf{K} + \mathbf{K}^*)}{4\pi r}\, dS , \tag{105b}$$

where

$$\rho^* = -\operatorname{div} \mathbf{P}, \tag{106a}$$

$$\kappa^* = \mathbf{P}.\mathbf{n}, \tag{106b}$$

$$\mathbf{J}^* = \operatorname{curl} \mathbf{I}/\mu_o, \tag{106c}$$

$$\mathbf{K}^* = \mathbf{I} \times \mathbf{n}/\mu_o. \tag{106d}$$

A comparison with (37) and (51) reveals that $\rho + \rho^* = \bar{\omega}$ and $\mathbf{J} + \mathbf{J}^* = \bar{\mathbf{j}}$, so that equations (105) might have been anticipated by reference to equations (8) and (12) of 1.3.

It is obvious from the form of the potential Φ that the corresponding value of $\mathbf{E}$ is, at all points inside and outside the body, exactly the same as would be produced (in free space) by supplementing the extrinsic densities ρ and κ with a volume distribution of charges of density ρ^* within V and a surface distibution of density κ^* on S. Similarly the corresponding value of $\mathbf{B}$ would be reproduced by supplementing $\mathbf{J}$ and $\mathbf{K}$ with a system of currents of volume density $\mathbf{J}^*$ within V and surface density $\mathbf{K}^*$ on S. Thus, for example, the charge distribution specified by ρ, ρ^*, κ and κ^* may be taken as a model of a dielectric body for the purpose of calculating $\mathbf{F}$ and $\mathbf{\Gamma}$.

In the magnetic case, the model specified by $\mathbf{J}$, $\mathbf{J}^*$, $\mathbf{K}$ and $\mathbf{K}^*$ reproduces the magnetic induction, $\mathbf{B}$, at all points inside and outside the surface S. It is also possible to construct a different model that reproduces the magnetic field, $\mathbf{H}$, at all interior and exterior points. The relationship $\mathbf{H} = (\mathbf{B} - \mathbf{I})/\mu_o$ holds both inside and outside the material body, whilst from Helmholtz's theorem

$$\mathbf{I} = -\operatorname{grad}\left\{\iiint_V \frac{\operatorname{div}\mathbf{I}}{4\pi r}\,dV - \oiint_S \frac{\mathbf{I}.\mathbf{n}}{4\pi r}\,dS\right\}$$

$$+\operatorname{curl}\left\{\iiint_V \frac{\operatorname{curl}\mathbf{I}}{4\pi r}\,dV + \oiint_S \frac{\mathbf{I}\times\mathbf{n}}{4\pi r}\,dS\right\}, \tag{107}$$

so that, from (103b), (104b), (107) and (53b)

$$\mathbf{H} = -\operatorname{grad}\Phi_M + \frac{1}{\mu_o}\operatorname{curl}\mathbf{A}_M, \tag{108a}$$

where

$$\Phi_M = \iiint_V \frac{-\operatorname{div}\mathbf{I}}{4\pi\mu_o r}\,dV + \oiint_S \frac{\mathbf{I}\,.\,\mathbf{n}}{4\pi\mu_o r}\,dS, \tag{108b}$$

$$\mathbf{A}_M = \iiint_V \frac{\mu_o \mathbf{J}}{4\pi r}\,dV + \oiint_S \frac{\mu_o \mathbf{K}}{4\pi r}\,dS. \tag{108c}$$

If such things as magnetic monopoles existed then (108b) would be recognisable as the magnetic scalar potential of a distribution of poles in free space of volume density† $\rho_M^* = -\operatorname{div}\mathbf{I}$ and surface density $\kappa_M^* = \mathbf{I}\,.\,\mathbf{n}$, whilst (108c) is just the vector potential appropriate, in free space, to the extrinsic current densities **J** and **K**. Such an arrangement of poles would constitute a model in which the magnetic field, **H**, would be correctly reproduced at all points inside and outside the surface *S*. Thus the equivalent pole model specified by **J**, **K**, ρ_M^* and κ_M^* reproduces **H** and $\mathbf{B} = (\mu_o\mathbf{H})$ outside *S* and **H** inside, whilst the equivalent current model specified by **J**, **J***, **K** and **K*** reproduces **H** and **B** outside *S* and **B** inside.‡ Either model may be used for the purpose of calculating **F** or **Γ**.

To calculate the force on the polarity $\kappa_M^*\,dS$ located on the surface element $d\mathbf{S}$ in the equivalent pole model it is necessary to know the field that would exist there if the element were removed, since no force can be exerted on the element by its own field. Consider first the case in which the surface current, **K**, is zero. The self field is, from symmetry considerations, equal, but oppositely directed, on opposite sides of the element of surface, whilst if κ_M^* were zero at the element the field would be continuous across it. It therefore follows that the effective field acting on the element may be found by subtracting from **H′**, or adding to **H**, one half of the discontinuity of field across the surface to give

$$\mathbf{H}' - \frac{\kappa_M^*}{2\mu_o}\mathbf{n} = \mathbf{H} + \frac{\kappa_M^*}{2\mu_o}\mathbf{n} = \tfrac{1}{2}(\mathbf{H}' + \mathbf{H}), \tag{109}$$

† ρ_M^* would therefore correspond to a magnetic multipole of zero order.

‡ The pole model is consistent with an elementary magnetic dipole of doublet form and it therefore leads, for $\mathbf{J} = \mathbf{K} = 0$, to the use of a magnetic scalar potential Φ_M (i.e. $\mathbf{A}_M = 0$), whilst the current model is consistent with an Ampèrian current loop and leads to the use of a vector potential.

where the prime is again used to distinguish the field, $\mathbf{H}'$, outside S from the field, $\mathbf{H}$, inside S (in this equivalent pole model $\mathbf{H}'$ and $\mathbf{H}$ are also respectively the fields outside and inside the material body). The corresponding force on the element is

$$\kappa_M^*\left(\mathbf{H}' - \frac{\kappa_M^*}{2\mu_o}\mathbf{n}\right)dS = \kappa_M^*\left(\mathbf{H} + \frac{\kappa_M^*}{2\mu_o}\mathbf{n}\right)dS = \tfrac{1}{2}\kappa_M^*(\mathbf{H}' + \mathbf{H})\,dS. \quad (110)$$

In a similar way it may be shown (Problem 4) that if $\mathbf{K} \neq 0$ the force on the element $d\mathbf{S}$ due to the presence of the polarity of density κ_M^* and the extrinsic surface current of density $\mathbf{K}$ is given by

$$d\mathbf{F}_1 = \tfrac{1}{2}\kappa_M^*(\mathbf{H}' + \mathbf{H})\,dS + \tfrac{1}{2}\mu_o\mathbf{K} \times (\mathbf{H}' + \mathbf{H})\,dS. \quad (111)$$

The total magnetic ponderomotive force on the equivalent pole model, and therefore on the body, is thus

$$\mathbf{F}^m = \iiint_V [\rho_M^*\mathbf{H} + \mu_o\mathbf{J} \times \mathbf{H}]\,dV + \oint\!\!\oint_S [\tfrac{1}{2}\kappa_M^*(\mathbf{H}' + \mathbf{H}) + \tfrac{1}{2}\mu_o\mathbf{K} \times (\mathbf{H}' + \mathbf{H})]\,dS. \quad (112)$$

However, from the boundary conditions $\mu_o(\mathbf{H}' - \mathbf{H})\,.\,\mathbf{n} = \kappa_M^*$ and $\mathbf{n} \times (\mathbf{H}' - \mathbf{H}) = \mathbf{K}$,

$$\begin{aligned}\mathbf{H}' + \mathbf{H} = 2\mathbf{H} + (\mathbf{H}' - \mathbf{H}) &= 2\mathbf{H} + \frac{\kappa_M^*}{\mu_o}\mathbf{n} + \mathbf{K} \times \mathbf{n} \\ &= 2\mathbf{H} + [(\mathbf{H}' - \mathbf{H})\,.\,\mathbf{n}]\mathbf{n} + \mathbf{K} \times \mathbf{n},\end{aligned} \quad (113)$$

whilst $\mathbf{H}'\,.\,\mathbf{n} = \mu_r\mathbf{H}\,.\,\mathbf{n}$, so that

$$\begin{aligned}\mathbf{F}^m = &\iiint_V [\mu_o\mathbf{J} \times \mathbf{H} - \mathbf{H}\,\mathrm{div}\,\mathbf{I}]\,dV \\ &+ \oint\!\!\oint_S \tfrac{1}{2}\mu_o[(\mathbf{H}' - \mathbf{H})\,.\,\mathbf{n}(\mathbf{K} \times \mathbf{n}) + \mathbf{K} \times (\mathbf{H}' + \mathbf{H})]\,dS \\ &+ \oint\!\!\oint_S \mu_o\{(\mu_r - 1)\mathbf{H}(\mathbf{H}\,.\,\mathbf{n}) + \tfrac{1}{2}(\mu_r - 1)^2(\mathbf{H}\,.\,\mathbf{n})^2\mathbf{n}\}\,dS.\end{aligned} \quad (114)$$

In a similar way the equivalent current model (in which **B** is everywhere reproduced) may be used to show that the total magnetic ponderomotive force is given by

$$\mathbf{F}^m = \iiint_V [(\mathbf{J} + \mathbf{J}^*) \times \mathbf{B}]\, dV + \oiint_S [\tfrac{1}{2}(\mathbf{K} + \mathbf{K}^*) \times (\mathbf{B}' + \mathbf{B})]\, dS$$

$$= \iiint_V \left[\mathbf{J} \times \mathbf{B} + \left(\frac{1}{\mu_o} \operatorname{curl} \mathbf{I}\right) \times \mathbf{B}\right] dV$$

$$+ \oiint_S \tfrac{1}{2}\mu_o[(\mu_r - 1)(\mathbf{H}\,.\,\mathbf{n})(\mathbf{K} \times \mathbf{n}) + \mathbf{K} \times (\mathbf{H}' + \mathbf{H})]\, dS$$

$$+ \oiint_S \tfrac{1}{2}\mu_o[(\mu_r - 1)(\mathbf{K} \times \mathbf{H}) + \mathbf{K}^* \times (\mathbf{H}' + \mu_r\mathbf{H})$$

$$- (\mu_r - 1)(\mathbf{H}\,.\,\mathbf{n})(\mathbf{K} \times \mathbf{n})]\, dS, \qquad (115)$$

where the relationships $\mathbf{B}' = \mu_o\mathbf{H}'$ and $\mathbf{B} = \mu_o\mu_r\mathbf{H}$ have been used to derive the second form of **F**. However, the vectors **K** and **K*** may be eliminated from the last surface integral (Problem 5) to give

$$\mathbf{F}^m = \iiint_V \left[\mathbf{J} \times \mathbf{B} + \left(\frac{1}{\mu_o} \operatorname{curl} \mathbf{I}\right) \times \mathbf{B}\right] dV$$

$$+ \oiint_S \tfrac{1}{2}\mu_o[(\mathbf{H}' - \mathbf{H})\,.\,\mathbf{n}(\mathbf{K} \times \mathbf{n}) + \mathbf{K} \times (\mathbf{H}' + \mathbf{H})]\, dS$$

$$+ \oiint_S \mu_o\{\mu_r(1 - \mu_r)\mathbf{H}(\mathbf{H}\,.\,\mathbf{n}) - \tfrac{1}{2}[(1 - \mu_r^2)H^2$$

$$- (\mu_r - 1)^2(\mathbf{H}\,.\,\mathbf{n})^2]\mathbf{n}\}\, dS. \qquad (116)$$

The magnetic ponderomotive force is therefore given by either (114) or (116) and the integrands in these equations therefore define a pair of equivalent force systems.

If a pair of expressions for alternative force systems really are equivalent then it may be suspected that this equivalence follows from an application of general transformations rather than from a consideration of particular models of the magnetic material. This is actually the case, for the Maxwellian expression

$$\mathbf{F}^m = \oint\!\!\!\oint_S \mu_o[\mathbf{H}'(\mathbf{H}'.\mathbf{n}) - \tfrac{1}{2}H'^2\mathbf{n}]\,dS, \tag{117}$$

where S is the surface of the material body, may be transformed (Problem 5) into the expression

$$\mathbf{F}^m = \oint\!\!\!\oint_S \tfrac{1}{2}\mu_o[(\mathbf{H}' - \mathbf{H}).\mathbf{n}(\mathbf{K}\times\mathbf{n}) + \mathbf{K}\times(\mathbf{H}' + \mathbf{H})]\,dS$$

$$+ \oint\!\!\!\oint_S \mu_o\{\mu_r\mathbf{H}(\mathbf{H}.\mathbf{n}) - \tfrac{1}{2}[H^2 - (\mu_r - 1)^2(\mathbf{H}.\mathbf{n})^2]\mathbf{n}\}\,dS. \tag{118}$$

The first integral is clearly the same as the first surface integral in both (114) and (116). During a discussion of the case $\mathbf{K} = 0$, the second integral in (118) is written, in equation (48) of 3.4(c), as an expression that can be made to assume an infinite number of different forms by the addition of an arbitrary volume integral and the subtraction of an equivalent surface integral. With each of these forms is associated an equivalent force system and two of these are shown (equations (54) and (55) of 3.4) to correspond to the equivalent pole and current models discussed here. The advantage of this method is that it does not rely on a consideration of particular models of the magnetic material. A similar method permits the introduction of an infinite number of equivalent force systems for a polarized dielectric material without the necessity of considering models involving pole-currents—by a historical accident poles at rest are almost respectable, but poles in motion are distinctly heterodox!

In practical applications the Maxwellian expression (117) for the total ponderomotive force is usually the most convenient. This is not only because of the absence of volume forces but also because the surface of integration need not be coincident with the surface of the material body the force on which is required. As indicated in 2.2, there are obvious advantages in forming the surface, where possible, of elements that are part of, or perpendicular to, equipotential surfaces. Once the field conditions at points external to the body have been established, the calculation of the total ponderomotive force presents no difficulty and numerical integration can be used if necessary. Carpenter (1959) discusses the determination of the ponderomotive force from equation (117) and gives a number of interesting examples.

It may also be mentioned that it is sometimes possible to measure the total energy of a system consisting of a material body in a field and the means whereby the field is produced. For example, if a magnetizable body is in the vicinity of a coil carrying current, it is possible to calculate energy changes by making electrical measurements in the circuit containing the coil. If this is done for various positions of the body, the principle of virtual work may then be used to deduce the total ponderomotive force. Further details of this method are given by Tustin (1952).

In conclusion it should be noted that the equivalent force systems discussed above are equivalent only in the sense that they may be used as alternative systems for the purpose of calculating the total ponderomotive force **F** and torque **Γ**. Nothing has been said about the relationship of these systems to the actual distribution of force within a material body—indeed the occurrence of an infinite number of equivalent force systems precludes an immediate identification of the actual force distribution. The problem of how to specify the distribution of forces in general, and ponderomotive forces in particular, in solid bodies is considered in Chapters 3 and 4.

PROBLEMS 2

1. Show that the average current density $\bar{\mathbf{j}}$ of 2.3 is given by

$$\bar{\mathbf{j}} = \mathbf{J} + \frac{\partial}{\partial t}[\mathbf{P} - \operatorname{Div} \mathbf{Q}] + \frac{1}{\mu_o} \operatorname{curl} \mathbf{I},$$

where

$$\mathbf{I}/N = \tfrac{1}{2}\mu_o \iiint_{\tau'} \mathbf{r}'' \times \mathbf{j}\, d\tau'$$

is the magnetic dipole moment of a single molecule [Rosenfeld (1951) p. 22].

2. If a scalar function f and its first and second derivatives are finite, continuous and single-valued functions of the coordinates

and if f either vanishes identically for large r or becomes equal to $\Gamma(0, \phi)/r^n$, show that

$$f = -\frac{1}{4\pi}\iiint_{\infty}\frac{\Delta f}{r}\,dV,$$

provided $r > 2$ [Page and Adams (1940) p. 53].

3. Show that

$$\iiint_{\infty}\frac{[\Box f]_{\text{ret}}}{r}\,dV = \iiint_{\infty}\frac{\Delta[f]_{\text{ret}}}{r}\,dV,$$

where $[\;]_{\text{ret}}$ indicates retardation [O'Rahilly (1938) p. 19].

4. From the boundary conditions $\mu_o(\mathbf{H}' - \mathbf{H})\,.\,\mathbf{n} = \kappa_M^*$ and $\mathbf{n} \times (\mathbf{H}' - \mathbf{H}) = \mathbf{K}$, establish the relationship

$$\mathbf{H}' - \mathbf{H} = \frac{\kappa_M^*}{\mu_o}\mathbf{n} + \mathbf{K} \times \mathbf{n}\,.$$

Consider a combined surface distribution of poles and currents in which the pole distribution and the current distribution are located on two separate surfaces that are everywhere a negligible distance apart. Show that if the inner surface distribution consists of poles, the combined force on two contiguous elements of area dS of the two distributions is

$$d\mathbf{F}_2 = \kappa_M^*\left(\mathbf{H} + \frac{\kappa_M^*}{2\mu_o}\mathbf{n}\right)dS + \mu_o\mathbf{K} \times \left(\mathbf{H} + \frac{\kappa_M^*}{\mu_o}\mathbf{n} + \tfrac{1}{2}\mathbf{K} \times \mathbf{n}\right)dS,$$

whereas if the inner surface distribution consists of currents it is

$$d\mathbf{F}_3 = \mu_o\mathbf{K} \times (\mathbf{H} + \tfrac{1}{2}\mathbf{K} \times \mathbf{n})\,dS + \kappa_M^*\left(\mathbf{H} + \mathbf{K} \times \mathbf{n} + \frac{\kappa_M^*}{2\mu_o}\mathbf{n}\right)dS\,.$$

Verify that both these vectors differ from

$$d\mathbf{F}_1 = \tfrac{1}{2}\kappa_M^*(\mathbf{H}' + \mathbf{H})\,dS + \tfrac{1}{2}\mu_o\mathbf{K} \times (\mathbf{H}' + \mathbf{H})\,dS$$

by the quantity

$$d\mathbf{F}_1 - d\mathbf{F}_2 = \tfrac{1}{2}\kappa_M^*(\mathbf{K} \times \mathbf{n})\,dS - \mu_o\mathbf{K} \times \frac{\kappa_M^*}{2\mu_o}\mathbf{n}\,dS = d\mathbf{F}_3 - d\mathbf{F}_1\,,$$

which is zero and which represents the sum of the force on the surface element of polarity due to the self field of the contiguous element of current and the force on the surface element of current due to the self field of the contiguous element of polarity.

5. Substitute for **K** and **K*** from

$$\mathbf{K} = \mathbf{n} \times (\mathbf{H}' - \mathbf{H}),$$

$$\mathbf{K}^* = \mathbf{I} \times \mathbf{n}/\mu_o = (\mu_r - 1)(\mathbf{H} \times \mathbf{n})$$

and use the boundary condition $(\mathbf{H}' - \mu_r\mathbf{H}) \cdot \mathbf{n} = 0$ and the vector identity

$$(\mathbf{U} \times \mathbf{V}) \times \mathbf{W} = (\mathbf{W} \cdot \mathbf{U})\mathbf{V} - (\mathbf{W} \cdot \mathbf{V})\mathbf{U}$$

to show that

$$\tfrac{1}{2}[(\mu_r - 1)(\mathbf{K} \times \mathbf{H}) + \mathbf{K}^* \times (\mathbf{H}' + \mu_r\mathbf{H}) - (\mu_r - 1)(\mathbf{H} \cdot \mathbf{n})(\mathbf{K} \times \mathbf{n})]$$
$$= \mu_r(1 - \mu_r)\mathbf{H}(\mathbf{H} \cdot \mathbf{n}) - \tfrac{1}{2}[(1 - \mu_r^2)H^2 - (\mu_r - 1)^2(\mathbf{H} \cdot \boldsymbol{n})^2]\mathbf{n}.$$

Use the vector identity and the relationship

$$\mathbf{H}' - \mathbf{H} = (\mu_r - 1)(\mathbf{H} \cdot \mathbf{n})\mathbf{n} + \mathbf{K} \times \mathbf{n}$$

to show that

$$\tfrac{1}{2}\mathbf{K} \times \{[(\mathbf{H}' - \mathbf{H}) \cdot \mathbf{n}]\mathbf{n} + (\mathbf{H}' + \mathbf{H})\}$$

$$= \{\mathbf{H}'(\mathbf{H}' \cdot \mathbf{n}) - \tfrac{1}{2}H'^2\mathbf{n}\} - \{\mu_r\mathbf{H}(\mathbf{H} \cdot \mathbf{n})$$
$$- \tfrac{1}{2}[H^2 - (\mu_r - 1)^2(\mathbf{H} \cdot \mathbf{n})^2]\mathbf{n}\}.$$

CHAPTER 3

The Elastic Behaviour of Solid Bodies

3.1 The mechanical stress tensor

In order to discuss the distribution of the ponderomotive force in a material body in a field, it is first necessary to examine how the system of stresses in a solid body is specified. The first distinction that must be made is between *extrinsic* and *internal* interactions, and this is clearly brought out by the simple example of a weight supported in the earth's gravitational field by a vertical cable. Focussing attention on the cable as an elastic body, the weight constitutes an *extrinsic* load or traction: the generalization of such an extrinsic load for a three-dimensional body is an extrinsic surface traction. But the cable itself is not weightless and each volume element of the cable is also subject to the earth's gravitational field. This constitutes an extrinsic body force, which is often referred to as a volume force. The extrinsic body and surface forces tend to stretch the cable and this tendency is opposed by *internal* forces resulting from the mutual interaction of pairs of particles that are located in the interior of the material. In a continuum theory, such as elasticity, these internal interactions are not considered explicitly but are dealt with by the introduction of a stress hypothesis. In the present example the stress hypothesis is that the cable is in a state of tension, so that at any point along its length those parts of the cable that lie near to the point but respectively above and below it exert equal and opposite forces on each other. The tension is in this case operationally defined, for if the cable is cut additional mechanical forces may be introduced at the cut to restore equilibrium. It may be noted that the utility of the stress hypothesis is connected with the further assumption of a local constitutive relation—that the extension of the cable is directly related (e.g. proportional) to the tension.

A similar procedure is adopted in specifying the stress distribution within a three-dimensional material body. The extrinsic volume force acting on a volume element dV will be denoted by $\mathbf{f}\,dV$ and, for generality, it will also be assumed that there is an extrinsic volume couple $\mathbf{L}\,dV$ acting on the volume element. (It is convenient to introduce $\mathbf{L}$ at this point although, in fact, it is necessary to consider a volume moment only for materials that are significantly polarizable or magnetizable.) The bounding surface S of the body will, in general, be subject to extrinsic surface tractions $\mathbf{T}$ (per unit area). Surface couples are, however, excluded because the corresponding forces are assumed to be bounded, that is of finite magnitude. Since a couple is envisaged as a pair of equal and opposite parallel forces separated by a moment arm, the moment of the couple vanishes as the moment arm approaches zero if the forces are bounded. The stress hypothesis is introduced by considering an element of surface $d\boldsymbol{\sigma}$ lying within the body itself, so that those parts of the medium which lie near to $d\boldsymbol{\sigma}$ but on opposite sides of it exert forces on each other. Forces are therefore transmitted across the element $d\boldsymbol{\sigma}$ and it is clear that the force transmitted across $d\boldsymbol{\sigma}$ will be proportional to $d\sigma$ and will consist of an action and an equal and opposite reaction. With a 'normal-outwards' convention for $d\boldsymbol{\sigma}$, it may be assumed that the force exerted across $d\boldsymbol{\sigma}$ by the matter outside σ on the matter within is represented by a vector $\mathbf{t}\,d\sigma$.

Now consider a small parallelepiped bounded by planes normal to the three coordinate axes as indicated in Fig. 3.1. The stress across the face A is given by some *vector* $-\mathbf{t}^x$ (the normal is in the direction of x decreasing) so that the force on that face has components

$$-t_x^x\,dy\,dz\,,\qquad -t_y^x\,dy\,dz\,,\qquad -t_z^x\,dy\,dz\,.$$

The force on the face B has components

$$\left[t_x^x+\frac{\partial t_x^x}{\partial x}dx\right]dy\,dz\,,\quad \left[t_y^x+\frac{\partial t_y^x}{\partial x}dx\right]dy\,dz\,,\quad \left[t_z^x+\frac{\partial t_z^x}{\partial x}dx\right]dy\,dz\,.$$

The resultant force acting on the parallelepiped due to stresses acting across these two planes thus has components

$$\frac{\partial t_x^x}{\partial x}dx\,dy\,dz\,,\qquad \frac{\partial t_y^x}{\partial x}dx\,dy\,dz\,,\qquad \frac{\partial t_z^x}{\partial x}dx\,dy\,dz\,.$$

Taking the other four faces into account, the x-component of the force due to stresses acting across its surfaces is

$$\frac{\partial t_x^x}{\partial x} dx\, dy\, dz + \frac{\partial t_x^y}{\partial y} dy\, dx\, dz + \frac{\partial t_x^z}{\partial z} dz\, dx\, dy\,.$$

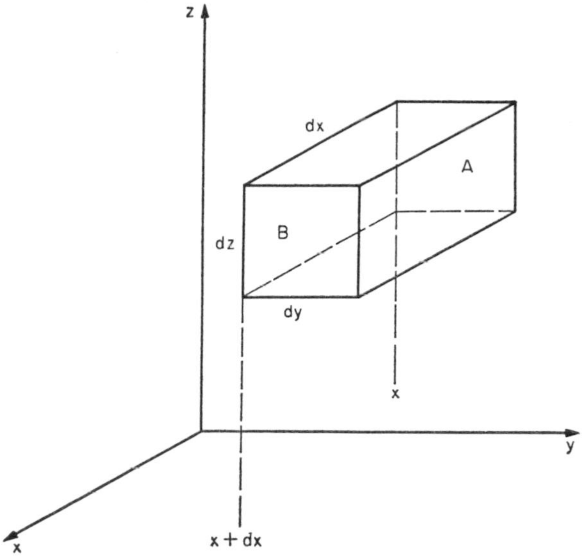

Fig. 3.1

Since the parallelepiped is in equilibrium this must be balanced by the x-component of the body force $\mathbf{f}\, dV = \mathbf{f}\, dx\, dy\, dz$, so that

$$f_x + \frac{\partial t_x^x}{\partial x} + \frac{\partial t_x^y}{\partial y} + \frac{\partial t_x^z}{\partial z} = 0\,. \tag{1a}$$

Similarly

$$f_y + \frac{\partial t_y^x}{\partial x} + \frac{\partial t_y^y}{\partial y} + \frac{\partial t_y^z}{\partial z} = 0 \tag{1b}$$

and

$$f_z + \frac{\partial t_z^x}{\partial x} + \frac{\partial t_z^y}{\partial y} + \frac{\partial t_z^z}{\partial z} = 0. \tag{1c}$$

Also, by taking moments about a line parallel to the z-axis and through the centre of the parallelepiped (where **f** and **L** may be supposed to act), it may be seen that

$$L_z\, dx\, dy\, dz + \frac{dx}{2}\left\{- t_y^x\, dy\, dz - \left[t_y^x + \frac{\partial t_y^x}{\partial x} dx\right] dy\, dz\right\}$$
$$+ \frac{dy}{2}\left\{t_x^y\, dx\, dz + \left[t_x^y + \frac{\partial t_x^y}{\partial y} dy\right] dx\, dz\right\} = 0. \tag{2}$$

Neglecting fourth-order small quantities in favour of third,

$$L_z - t_y^x + t_x^y = 0. \tag{3a}$$

Similarly,

$$L_x - t_z^y + t_y^z = 0 \tag{3b}$$

and

$$L_y - t_x^z + t_z^x = 0. \tag{3c}$$

It may now be asked: what force acts over an element of surface that is arbitrarily orientated? Since the limit as the area of the element tends to zero is to be considered, a surface of any shape may be chosen, for example, the triangular surface illustrated in Fig. 3.2 The tetrahedron $OABC$ is of volume $d\tau = k(d\sigma)^{3/2}$ (actually $k = \frac{1}{3}\sqrt{2n_x n_y n_z}$). To find the area of the face OAC, consider the perpendiculars OP' and BP'' from O and B on to the line AC. Both OP' and BP'' are perpendicular to AC. But OB is perpendicular to the plane OAC and therefore to AC. Thus OP', BP'' and OB are all perpendicular to AC—i.e. are coplanar—so that P' and P'' must coincide (at P say). Now

$$d\sigma = \tfrac{1}{2} AC\,.\,BP, \tag{4}$$

$$OAC = \tfrac{1}{2} AC\,.\,OP \tag{5}$$

and

$$OP = BP \cos \widehat{OPB} . \tag{6}$$

But the angle $\widehat{OPB}$ is the angle between the planes ABC and OAC,

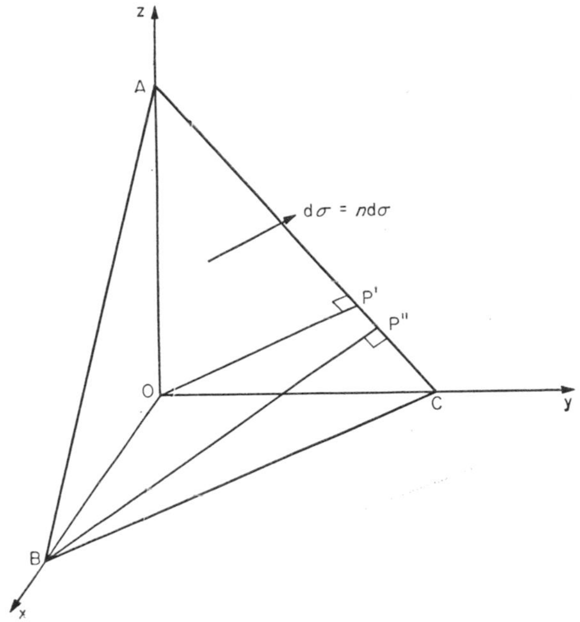

Fig. 3.2

which is the angle between their normals. Since the normals are **n** and the x-axis,

$$\cos \widehat{OPB} = n_x \tag{7}$$

and

$$OAC = n_x \, d\sigma . \tag{8}$$

Now let the force on the face $d\boldsymbol{\sigma}$ be $\mathbf{t}\, d\sigma$ and consider the equilibrium of the tetrahedron $OABC$. Resolving parallel to the x-axis,

$$f_x k(d\sigma)^{3/2} + t_x \, d\sigma - t_x^x n_x \, d\sigma - t_x^y n_y \, d\sigma - t_x^z n_z \, d\sigma = 0 . \tag{9}$$

Thus in the limit, as $d\sigma \to 0$,

$$t_x = t_x^x n_x + t_x^y n_y + t_x^z n_z \tag{10}$$

with similar expressions for t_y and t_z. The nine components

$$\begin{bmatrix} t_x^x & t_x^y & t_x^z \\ t_y^x & t_y^y & t_y^z \\ t_z^x & t_z^y & t_z^z \end{bmatrix}$$

are said to form the components of the stress tensor. Any set of nine quantities that describe a possible state of stress within a solid body must satisfy the six equations

$$f_x + \frac{\partial t_x^x}{\partial x} + \frac{\partial t_x^y}{\partial y} + \frac{\partial t_x^z}{\partial z} = 0,$$

$$f_y + \frac{\partial t_y^x}{\partial x} + \frac{\partial t_y^y}{\partial y} + \frac{\partial t_y^z}{\partial z} = 0,$$

$$f_z + \frac{\partial t_z^x}{\partial x} + \frac{\partial t_z^y}{\partial y} + \frac{\partial t_z^z}{\partial z} = 0, \tag{11a}$$

$$L_x - t_z^y + t_y^z = 0,$$

$$L_y - t_x^z + t_z^x = 0,$$

$$L_z - t_y^x + t_x^y = 0. \tag{11b}$$

The formulation of these equations may be considerably simplified by employing suffixes i, j, k, etc. which are assumed to run from 1 to 3, corresponding to axes $x_1 = x$, $x_2 = y$, $x_3 = z$. Thus the vector $\mathbf{H}$ is denoted by H_i, it being understood that all three components $H_1 = H_x$, $H_2 = H_y$, $H_3 = H_z$ are to be considered. For example, the equation $d\mathbf{S} = \mathbf{n}\, dS$ becomes $dS_i = n_i\, dS$, whilst the equation $\mathbf{B} = \mu\mathbf{H}$ becomes $B_i = \mu H_i$. However, the real value of this notation lies in the use of the Einstein summation convention, sometimes referred to as the 'dummy suffix notation'. This convention is that summation is implied over any repeated index. Thus

$$\alpha_i\beta_i = \sum_{i=1}^{3} \alpha_i\beta_i = \alpha_1\beta_1 + \alpha_2\beta_2 + \alpha_3\beta_3. \tag{12a}$$

and

$$\alpha_i\beta_i\gamma_j\delta_j = \sum_{i=1}^{3}\sum_{j=1}^{3}\alpha_i\beta_i\gamma_j\delta_j$$
$$= \alpha_1\beta_1\gamma_1\delta_1 + \alpha_1\beta_1\gamma_2\delta_2 + \alpha_1\beta_1\gamma_3\delta_3$$
$$+ \alpha_2\beta_2\gamma_1\delta_1 + \alpha_2\beta_2\gamma_2\delta_2 + \alpha_2\beta_2\gamma_3\delta_3$$
$$+ \alpha_3\beta_3\gamma_1\delta_1 + \alpha_3\beta_3\gamma_2\delta_2 + \alpha_3\beta_3\gamma_3\delta_3 . \qquad (12b)$$

The index is 'dummy' since it may be replaced by any other; thus

$$\alpha_i\beta_i = \alpha_s\beta_s \qquad (13a)$$

and

$$\alpha_i\beta_i\gamma_j\delta_k = \alpha_s\beta_s\gamma_j\delta_k . \qquad (13b)$$

Examples of the use of the dummy suffix notation are:

$$\mathbf{B}.d\mathbf{S} = B_1\,dS_1 + B_2\,dS_2 + B_3\,dS_3 = B_i\,dS_i = B_i n_i\,dS , \qquad (14a)$$

$$H^2 = H_i H_i , \qquad (14b)$$

$$\operatorname{div}\mathbf{B} = \frac{\partial B_1}{\partial x_1} + \frac{\partial B_2}{\partial x_2} + \frac{\partial B_3}{\partial x_3} = \frac{\partial B_i}{\partial x_i} . \qquad (14c)$$

Similarly, the integrand of equation (117) of 2.4, that is

$$d\mathbf{F}^m = \mu_o[(\mathbf{H}'.\mathbf{n})\mathbf{H}' - \tfrac{1}{2}H'^2\mathbf{n}]\,dS , \qquad (15)$$

may be written in the form

$$dF_i^m = \mu_o[H_i'H_j'n_j - \tfrac{1}{2}H_j'H_j'n_i]\,dS . \qquad (16)$$

Returning now to equations (11a) and replacing superscripts by second subscripts, the *set of three* equations of the type

$$f_x + \frac{\partial t_x^x}{\partial x} + \frac{\partial t_x^y}{\partial y} + \frac{\partial t_x^z}{\partial z} = 0 \qquad (17a)$$

becomes

$$f_i + \frac{\partial t_{ij}}{\partial x_j} = 0 . \qquad (17b)$$

It is also possible to write equations (11b) in a compact form, namely

$$L_i - \varepsilon_{ijk} t_{jk} = 0, \tag{18}$$

where the ε_{ijk} are the components of the *alternating tensor*, defined by the condition that $\varepsilon_{ijk} = 0$ if any two of i, j, k are equal, whilst if they are all unequal $\varepsilon_{ijk} = +1$ if the order i, j, k is cyclic and $\varepsilon_{ijk} = -1$ if the order is not cyclic. It may be noted that materials that are significantly polarizable or magnetizable are excluded from the present discussion so that, in fact, $\mathbf{L} = 0$ and equations (18) reduce to

$$t_{ij} = t_{ji}. \tag{19}$$

The stress tensor is then symmetrical and only six of its nine components are independent. As a final example of the use of the summation convention consider equations (9) of 2.1: if

$$\begin{aligned} U_x &= d_{11}, & U_y &= d_{12}, & U_z &= d_{13}, \\ U'_x &= d_{21}, & U'_y &= d_{22}, & U'_z &= d_{23}, \\ U''_x &= d_{31}, & U''_y &= d_{32}, & U''_z &= d_{33}, \end{aligned} \tag{20}$$

then the equations (13) of 2.1 may be written in the form

$$F_i = \oiint_S d_{ij}\, dS_j, \tag{21a}$$

whilst the d_{ij} themselves may be expressed in the form

$$d_{ij} = \varepsilon_o(E_i E_j - \tfrac{1}{2}E^2 \delta_{ij}), \tag{21b}$$

where δ_{ij} is the *Kronecker* delta, a quantity that is unity when $i = j$ and zero when $i \neq j$.

3.2 The strain tensor

To clarify how the state of strain is specified in a solid body, consider first the two-dimensional case of an extendible plane sheet. This is achieved by choosing an origin, fixed in space, and studying how the displacement of the points on the sheet varies with their coordinates, restricting the discussion to small displacements only. Let the point P, whose coordinates referred to axes fixed in space are x_1, x_2 before deformation, move to P', with coordinates $x_1 + u_1$, $x_2 + u_2$ after deformation. The vector u_i is therefore the displacement of P. To specify the strain at this point of the sheet it is convenient first to define the four quantities

$$e_{11} = \frac{\partial u_1}{\partial x_1}, \qquad e_{12} = \frac{\partial u_1}{\partial x_2},$$
$$e_{21} = \frac{\partial u_2}{\partial x_1}, \qquad e_{22} = \frac{\partial u_2}{\partial x_2}, \tag{22a}$$

or, collectively,

$$e_{ij} = \frac{\partial u_i}{\partial x_j} \qquad (i,j = 1,2). \tag{22b}$$

The e_{ij} are all dimensionless quantities, small compared with unity. To find their geometrical meanings, consider a point Q lying near P, such that $PQ = \Delta x_i$. After deformation Q moves to Q', and, clearly, $P'Q'$ is the sum of two vectors, $\Delta x_i + \Delta u_i$. Δu_i is the difference in displacement between the two points P and Q originally separated by Δx_i. Then, since the components of Δu_i are functions of position,

$$\Delta u_1 = \frac{\partial u_1}{\partial x_1}\Delta x_1 + \frac{\partial u_1}{\partial x_2}\Delta x_2, \tag{23a}$$

$$\Delta u_2 = \frac{\partial u_2}{\partial x_1}\Delta x_1 + \frac{\partial u_2}{\partial x_2}\Delta x_2, \tag{23b}$$

or, briefly,

$$\Delta u_i = \frac{\partial u_i}{\partial x_j}\Delta x_j = e_{ij}\,\Delta x_j. \tag{23c}$$

As Δu_i and Δx_j are both vectors it follows that e_{ij} is a tensor.

Consider now two special positions of the vector Δx_i, first parallel to Ox_1 (PQ_1) and then parallel to Ox_2 (PQ_2); this will reveal how a

E.M.F.—F

rectangular element at P is distorted. For PQ_1, $\Delta x_2 = 0$, so that

$$\Delta u_1 = \frac{\partial u_1}{\partial x_1}\Delta x_1 = e_{11}\Delta x_1 , \tag{24a}$$

$$\Delta u_2 = \frac{\partial u_2}{\partial x_1}\Delta x_1 = e_{21}\Delta x_1 . \tag{24b}$$

The meanings of Δu_1 and Δu_2 are indicated in Fig. 3.3.

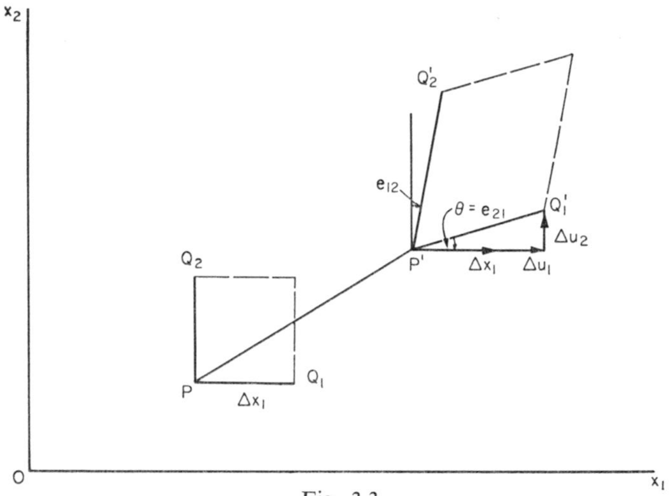

Fig. 3.3

It may be seen that e_{11} measures the extension per unit length of PQ_1 resolved along Ox_1, for

$$\frac{\Delta u_1}{\Delta x_1} = \frac{\partial u_1}{\partial x_1} = e_{11} . \tag{25}$$

The quantity e_{21} measures the anticlockwise rotation of PQ_1, for the angle through which it turns is given by

$$\tan\theta = \frac{\Delta u_2}{\Delta x_1 + \Delta u_1} . \tag{26a}$$

Since only small displacements are under consideration, u_1 and u_2 are small compared with x_1, and hence Δu_1 and Δu_2 are small compared with Δx_1. Thus

$$\theta = \frac{\Delta u_2}{\Delta x_1} - e_{21}\,. \tag{26b}$$

In a similar way, e_{22} equals the extension per unit length of PQ_2 in the Ox_2 direction, and e_{12} measures the (small) clockwise rotation of PQ_2 to $P'Q'_2$.

It may now be asked: is the tensor e_{ij} a satisfactory measure of the strain at the point P? For an affirmative answer it is clearly necessary that, when there is no distortion, all four components of e_{ij} should vanish. This does not in fact happen. For consider a simple rigid-body rotation of the sheet in its own plane, anticlockwise, through a *small* angle ϕ—as shown diagrammatically in Fig. 3.4.

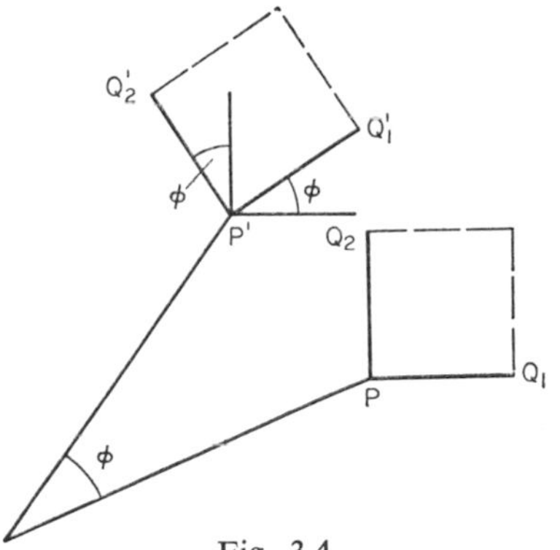

Fig. 3.4

The rotations of PQ_1 and PQ_2 are both ϕ anticlockwise, and hence, from the geometrical meanings of the e_{ij} established above,

$$\begin{aligned} e_{11} &= 0, \qquad e_{12} = -\phi, \\ e_{21} &= \phi, \qquad e_{22} = 0, \end{aligned} \tag{27a}$$

which may also be written in the form

$$e_{ij} = \begin{bmatrix} 0 & -\phi \\ \phi & 0 \end{bmatrix}. \tag{27b}$$

This is therefore a case in which, although there is no distortion of the sheet, e_{ij} does not vanish. To avoid this difficulty it is necessary to find a way of subtracting the part of e_{ij} corresponding to a rigid-body rotation.

Now any second-rank tensor can be expressed as the sum of a symmetrical and an antisymmetrical tensor. Thus e_{ij} may be written in the form

$$e_{ij} = E_{ij} + W_{ij}, \tag{28a}$$

where

$$E_{ij} = \tfrac{1}{2}(e_{ij} + e_{ji}) \tag{28b}$$

and

$$W_{ij} = \tfrac{1}{2}(e_{ij} - e_{ji}). \tag{28c}$$

The quantity E_{ij}, so defined, is a symmetrical tensor, for

$$E_{ij} = \tfrac{1}{2}(e_{ji} + e_{ij}) = E_{ji}, \tag{29a}$$

whilst W_{ij} is an antisymmetrical tensor, for

$$W_{ij} = -\tfrac{1}{2}(e_{ji} - e_{ij}) = -W_{ji}. \tag{29b}$$

However, it may be seen from (27) that the tensor representing a pure rotation is antisymmetrical, and it is therefore permissible to define the *symmetrical* part of e_{ij}, that is E_{ij}, as the *strain*. Thus, in full,

$$\begin{bmatrix} E_{11} & E_{12} \\ E_{12} & E_{22} \end{bmatrix} = \begin{bmatrix} e_{11} & \tfrac{1}{2}(e_{12} + e_{21}) \\ \tfrac{1}{2}(e_{12} + e_{21}) & e_{22} \end{bmatrix}. \tag{30}$$

The diagonal components of E_{ij} are the extensons per unit length parallel to Ox_1 and Ox_2. E_{12} measures the *tensor shear strain*; if two line elements are drawn parallel to Ox_1 and Ox_2 in the undeformed body the angle between them after deformation is $\tfrac{1}{2}\pi - 2E_{12}$. It may be noted that the tensor shear strain E_{12} is *one-half* of the change in angle between the two elements.

In a similar way three-dimensional strain is specified by nine tensor components

$$e_{ij} = \frac{\partial u_i}{\partial x_j} \quad (i, j = 1, 2, 3) \tag{31}$$

and the symmetrical strain tensor has nine components

$$E_{ij} = \tfrac{1}{2}(e_{ij} + e_{ji}), \tag{32}$$

only six of which are independent. The relationship between these components and the components, t_{ij}, of the stress tensor is discussed in the next section.

3.3 The relationship between stress and strain

According to the classical theory of elasticity (Love 1944) a linear relationship exists between the components of stress and strain, which may either be written in the form

$$t_{ij} = C_{ijkl}E_{kl} \tag{33a}$$

or in the reciprocal form

$$E_{ij} = S_{ijkl}t_{kl}, \tag{33b}$$

where the C_{ijkl} are the elastic stiffness constants and the S_{ijkl} the elastic compliance moduli. For an isotropic material these equations (representing a generalized Hooke's law) assume the following particularly simple form:

$$t_{ij} = \frac{Y\nu}{(1+\nu)(1-2\nu)}\varepsilon\delta_{ij} + \frac{Y}{1+\nu}E_{ij}, \tag{34a}$$

$$E_{ij} = -\frac{\nu}{Y}\Theta\delta_{ij} + \frac{1+\nu}{Y}t_{ij}, \tag{34b}$$

where Y is Young's modulus, ν is Poisson's ratio, $\varepsilon = E_{kk}$ is the dilatation and $\Theta = t_{kk}$.

In an elastic body that is subjected to a prescribed system of body forces, $\mathbf{f}\,dV$, and a prescribed system of surface tractions, $\mathbf{T}\,dS$, the stress tensor must satisfy the equations

$$f_i + \frac{\partial t_{ij}}{\partial x_j} = 0 \tag{35}$$

everywhere within the body and must satisfy the boundary conditions

$$t_{ij}n_j = T_i \tag{36}$$

at the surface of the body. It is clear that the f_i and the T_i are not completely independent, for equation (35) was established on the hypothesis that the body is in equilibrium, so that f_i and T_i must be such as to satisfy the equation

$$\iiint_V f_i\,dV + \oint\!\!\oint_S T_i\,dS = 0 \tag{37}$$

(which is derivable from (35) and (36) by the Gauss divergence theorem). However, equations (35) and (36) are not sufficient to specify the stress tensor completely and they must be augmented by the conditions of compatibility. The conditions of compatibility are a consequence of the fact that the elastic displacements of a certain point with respect to another point can be calculated by integrating the strains along a path between these points, and the result must be independent of the choice of the path. This leads to the following compatibility equations (Sokolnikoff 1956)

$$\frac{\partial^2 E_{ij}}{\partial x_k \partial x_l} + \frac{\partial^2 E_{kl}}{\partial x_i \partial x_j} = \frac{\partial^2 E_{jl}}{\partial x_i \partial x_k} + \frac{\partial^2 E_{ik}}{\partial x_j \partial x_l}, \tag{38}$$

which reduce, essentially, to only six equations when permutations and identities are eliminated. These conditions can also be expressed in terms of the components of the stress tensor: for an isotropic solid the resulting equations are

$$\nabla^2 t_{ij} + \frac{1}{1+\nu}\frac{\partial^2 \Theta}{\partial x_i \partial x_j} = -\frac{\nu}{1-\nu}\delta_{ij}\frac{\partial f_k}{\partial x_k} - \left[\frac{\partial f_i}{\partial x_j} + \frac{\partial f_j}{\partial x_i}\right], \tag{39}$$

which are known as the Beltrami-Michell compatibility equations. Thus, in order to determine the state of stress in the interior of an elastic body subject to prescribed body and surface forces it is necessary to solve the system of equations consisting of (35) and (39) subject to the boundary conditions (36). It should be noted that equations (35) and (36) are not themselves sufficient to specify t_{ij} uniquely, since it is possible to add to t_{ij} any tensor β_{ij} that satisfies $\partial\beta_{ij}/\partial x_j = 0$ and $\beta_{ij} n_j = 0$.†

3.4 Stresses in dielectric or magnetic bodies

(*a*) *Body forces and surface stresses.* In the discussion in 3.1 on how the system of stresses in an ordinary solid body is specified, a dis-

† For example, if a weight $W = w\pi R^2$ is supported by a weightless homogeneous cylindrical cable of radius R, a solution that satisfies (35) and (36) is

$$t_{11} = a[1-(x_1^2+3x_2^2)/R^2],\ t_{22} = a[1-(3x_1^2+x_2^2)/R^2],$$
$$t_{33} = w, \quad t_{12} = 2ax_1x_2/R^2, \quad t_{23} = t_{31} = 0,$$

where the x_3-axis is the vertical cable axis and a is arbitrary. However, (34b) reveals that $E_{33} = w/Y - (2a\nu/Y)[1-2(x_1^2+x_2^2)/R^2]$, and both symmetry and equation (39) require that a be zero.

tinction was made between *extrinsic* interactions, that is surface stresses **T** and body forces **f** dV, and *internal* interactions, which are dealt with by the introduction of a stress hypothesis and, consequently, a stress vector, **t**. For a dielectric body in an electric field or a magnetic body in a magnetic field, the total ponderomotive force is, in general, non-zero and it is therefore necessary to allow for an alteration in the vectors **f** and **t**. It will be assumed for the present that a formulation in terms of a modified body force density and a modified stress vector is acceptable, is sufficient and is unique: these three assumptions are, however, examined critically in 4.2. Thus, for example, in the magnetic case, there would be a specifically magnetic body force density, **g**, and a specifically magnetic stress vector, **m**. In addition, since the magnetic conditions vary rapidly across the surface of the body it may also be necessary to introduce a specifically magnetic surface stress **Λ**, and this will be included for the sake of generality. The phrase 'specifically magnetic' is taken to mean existing by virtue of the body being magnetized: apart from a specification of the reference state (discussed below) it is convenient to defer any more detailed definition until Chapter 4.

In using the symbols **g**, **m** and **Λ** (and, later, m_{ij}), the electric and magnetic cases will not usually be distinguished except by the context in which they occur: when the distinction is necessary it will be achieved by using superscripts thus, $\mathbf{g}^e$ and $\mathbf{g}^m$. For a magnetic material, as for an ordinary material, the existence of a stress vector implies the existence of a stress tensor, and this may be demonstrated by considering, as in 3.1, the (kinetic) equilibrium of a tetrahedron as its dimensions tend to zero. In this case, of course, the tetrahedron is not in static equilibrium, but the rate of change of momentum of the matter contained therein may be neglected, as it tends to zero in the same way as the body force associated with the force density $\mathbf{f} + \mathbf{g}$, that is as $(d\sigma)^{3/2}$. In this way it is possible to define, at points *within* the body, a tensor, m_{ij}, which specifies the stress that accompanies the magnetization of the body. This tensor is not necessarily symmetrical and the intrinsic volume couple, **L**, introduced in 3.1, is not necessarily zero.

In considering the kinetic equilibrium of an infinitesimal parallelepiped, as in 3.1, the sum of all the forces acting on the matter within the volume element is now not zero but is equal to the rate of change of momentum of this matter, and (using (17b) of 3.1) this is in turn equal, per unit volume, to

$$f_i + g_i + \frac{\partial t_{ij}}{\partial x_j} + \frac{\partial m_{ij}}{\partial x_j} = g_i + \frac{\partial m_{ij}}{\partial x_j}. \tag{40}$$

The force on any interior volume element may be obtained by integration and, in particular, the force on the whole body is given by

$$\begin{aligned} F_i &= \iiint_V \left[g_i + \frac{\partial m_{ij}}{\partial x_j} \right] dV \\ &= \iiint_V g_i \, dV + \oiint_S m_{ij} n_j \, dS \\ &= \iiint_V g_i \, dV + \oiint_S \Lambda_i \, dS, \end{aligned} \tag{41}$$

where the last equality is obtained by using the boundary condition

$$m_{ij} n_j = \Lambda_i, \tag{42}$$

which is necessary to prevent a finite force from operating on an infinitesimally small element of mass at the boundary. It may be noted that in evaluating the volume integral of **g** in (41) the effect of a rapid variation in **g** at the bounding surface of the body is to be ignored since this contribution is precisely the surface stress **Λ**.

The tensor m_{ij} is clearly not the stress in the practical situation in which additional mechanical forces are applied to prevent the body moving under the action of the total ponderomotive force (and couple). For example, if overall static equilibrium is maintained by the application of *additional* mechanical surface stresses **T***, then the stress tensor is $t_{ij} + m'_{ij}$ where m'_{ij} satisfies the equations

$$g_i + \frac{\partial m'_{ij}}{\partial x_j} = 0 \tag{43}$$

and the boundary condition

$$m'_{ij} n_j = \Lambda_i + T_i^*, \tag{44}$$

whilst the corresponding strain tensor is subject to compatibility equations of the form (38). Hence m'_{ij} is not specified by the vectors **g** and **Λ**: it must be dependent on the T_i^*, that is the tensor m'_{ij}

depends upon the details of the mechanical arrangements that are made to prevent movement of the body as a whole. For example, if a rod-shaped magnetic body is being drawn towards the pole gap of a powerful electromagnet (under the action of a body force density), it may be placed in tension by holding it at one end and compression by holding it at the other. This difficulty is a trivial one in the sense that it can be removed by specifying the mechanical arrangements. Even if this is done, however, equations (43) and (44) do not serve to determine m'_{ij}, any more than (35) and (36) alone served to determine t_{ij} in 3.3. Compatibility equations of the form

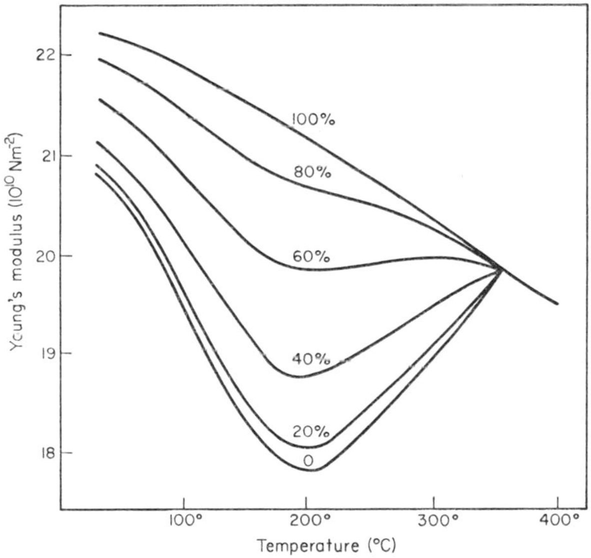

Fig. 3.5

(39) involving the m_{ij} can not now be derived from (38) because, as indicated below, the relationship between stress and strain is, in general, dependent in a complicated way on the magnetization. It is therefore pointless to attempt to obtain a general expression for m_{ij} or m'_{ij}: in the general case the physically significant quantities are the vectors **g** and **Λ**. Furthermore, it is not to be expected that the tensor m'_{ij} will be expressible in a general form that is dependent only on local magnetic conditions, because the stress depends on the

shape of the body via the surface stresses **Λ**. The corresponding shape dependence of the deformation of the body is known (in the magnetic case) as the form effect and this phenomenon is considered in more detail in Chapter 6. Although it is often possible to arrange matters so that the contribution of the form effect to the overall magnetic deformation of the body is small, its existence emphasizes the importance of specifying the state of stress of a material body by means of the vectors **g** and **Λ**.

(*b*) *The reference state*. In referring to **g** and **Λ** as additional specifically magnetic quantities, no explicit mention was made of any reference state, although a reference state is, of course, needed to justify the use of the word additional. By implication the reference state is one in which the body is not magnetized, but it is not sufficient to refer to a body in zero applied field for there is no reason to suppose that the stress within an unmagnetized body will be the same as that within the same body at remenance—nor indeed between two states of the body achieved by different demagnetization procedures. To define the reference state unambiguously it is, in fact, necessary to refer not to an unmagnetized body but to a non-magnetic body—that is one in which the magnetic interactions have been annihilated. This state, in which there are no magnetic interactions to deform the body, is not, of course, realizable experimentally, but the most obvious method of evaluating the deformation associated with the destruction of the spontaneous magnetization is to measure the thermal expansion of the body over a temperature range that includes the Curie point. The deformation of the material associated with the appearance of the spontaneous magnetization may then be seen superimposed on the normal thermal expansion. There are also indirect methods of estimating this deformation (Lee 1955).

That this choice of reference state is the natural one may also be seen by performing experiments to measure the relation between strain and applied stress in magnetic materials. Experiments to measure the elastic constants of magnetic materials give different results for differing magnetic conditions and Fig. 3.5 shows the temperature variation of the apparent Young's modulus of polycrystalline nickel† for a number of fields which magnetize the material

† For iron the effect is much smaller, whilst for some alloys the effect is masked by a large forced volume magnetostriction (Lee 1955).

to certain percentage fractions of the saturation value. For saturating fields the curve is sensibly continuous through the Curie point and this curve represents the normal variation of Young's modulus with temperature for the non-magnetic material, i.e. that appropriate to a nickel sample in which the magnetic interactions have been annihilated.

For dielectric materials in which the polarization is distortional, that is ionic or electronic, the reference state is merely that in which the applied field is zero. In distortional polarization the elementary dipole moments are produced by the applied field separating charges of opposite sign or modifying a neutral charge distribution. The equilibrium state is therefore the unique one of zero dipole moment and this is a satisfactory reference state. For ferroelectric materials, however, the polarization within a ferroelectric domain has a finite value even when the bulk polarization is zero and it is therefore necessary to adopt the type of reference state discussed above for magnetic materials.

(*c*) *Expressions for* **g** *and* **Λ**. Whatever the form of **g** and **Λ**, the total ponderomotive force is known: for example, in the magnetic case it is

$$\mathbf{F} = \oiint_{S'} \mu_o \{\mathbf{H}'(\mathbf{H}' . \mathbf{n}) - \tfrac{1}{2} H'^2 \mathbf{n}\}\, dS\,, \tag{46}$$

where the integration is performed over a surface S' that encloses the body but is not necessarily coincident with it, and where the primes in the integrand indicate that the field is evaluated at points outside the body. It may be noted that **F** is a linear vector function of **n**, and it is this fact that makes the integrand derivable from a tensor —the Maxwell stress tensor for free space. (In other words (46) may be written, for any S', in a form analogous to (21a) because **F** is a linear vector function of **n**.) Equation (46) is valid when S' is any surface enclosing the body and in particular when it is the surface outside and immediately adjacent to the surface, S, of the body. Equally the integration could be performed over a surface immediately within the surface of the body but to preserve the notation according to which field quantities occurring in the integrand are evaluated at the surface over which the integration is performed it is necessary to formulate this integral in terms of the field **H** within the material. Since **H** and **H**′ are related, in the absence of surface currents, by the boundary conditions

$$\begin{aligned} \mu_r H_n &= H'_n, \\ H_t &= H'_t, \end{aligned} \tag{47}$$

the total force on the body may be written as

$$\begin{aligned} \mathbf{F} &= \oint\!\!\oint_S \mu_o\{\mathbf{H}'(\mathbf{H}'.\mathbf{n}) - \tfrac{1}{2}H'^2\mathbf{n}\}\,dS \\ &= \oint\!\!\oint_S \mu_o\{\mu_r\mathbf{H}(\mathbf{H}.\mathbf{n}) - \tfrac{1}{2}H^2\mathbf{n}\}\,dS + \oint\!\!\oint_S \tfrac{1}{2}\mu_o(\mu_r - 1)^2(\mathbf{H}.\mathbf{n})^2\mathbf{n}\,dS \\ &= \iiint_V \mathbf{g}^\dagger dV + \oint\!\!\oint_S \mathbf{\Lambda}^*\,dS, \end{aligned} \tag{48}$$

where the transformation from a surface integral to a volume integral has been effected by (17) of 2.1 and where

$$g_i^\dagger = \frac{\partial}{\partial x_j}\mu_o\{\mu_r H_i H_j - \tfrac{1}{2}H^2\delta_{ij}\}, \tag{49a}$$

$$\Lambda_i^* = \tfrac{1}{2}\mu_o(\mu_r - 1)^2(H_k n_k)^2 n_i. \tag{49b}$$

Comparing (48) with (41) it is possible to write, without loss of generality,

$$g_i = g_i^\dagger + k_i, \tag{50a}$$

$$\Lambda_i = \Lambda_i^* + \bar{k}_i, \tag{50b}$$

where k_i and $\bar{k}_i$ are the components of vectors that satisfy the equation

$$\iiint_V \mathbf{k}\,dV + \oint\!\!\oint_S \bar{\mathbf{k}}\,dS = 0. \tag{51}$$

(The use of specific symbols, $g_i^\dagger$ and $\mathbf{\Lambda}_i^*$, for the terms in which the field dependence is exhibited explicitly is merely a matter of convenience and is without further significance.) Similarly, a consideration of the total ponderomotive torque (Problem 3) reveals that **k** and $\bar{\mathbf{k}}$ also satisfy the equation

$$\iiint_V [\mathbf{L} + \mathbf{r} \times \mathbf{k}]\, dV + \oiint_S \mathbf{r} \times \bar{\mathbf{k}}\, dS = 0, \tag{52}$$

where $\mathbf{L}$ is the intrinsic volume couple.

It is now possible to interrelate the vectors $\mathbf{k}$ and $\bar{\mathbf{k}}$, and to show that $\mathbf{\Lambda} \neq 0$. To do this it is necessary to introduce the assumptions, discussed further at a later stage (in 4.3), that the body force density $\mathbf{g}$, and therefore $\mathbf{k}$, depends only on magnetic conditions at the volume element dV and not, for example, on the disposition of the surface S with respect to dV, and that the surface stress $\mathbf{\Lambda}$, and therefore $\bar{\mathbf{k}}$, depends only on magnetic conditions at the surface element and on the direction of the normal $\mathbf{n}$. Although $\mathbf{k}$ is (otherwise) an arbitrary vector function, it can always be written, by means of Helmholtz's theorem in the form $-\text{grad}\,\Phi + \text{curl}\,\mathbf{A}$ where, as indicated in equations (19), (20) and (21) of 1.5, Φ and $\mathbf{A}$ are defined in terms of source and circulation densities $s = \text{div}\,\mathbf{k}$ and $\mathbf{c} = \text{curl}\,\mathbf{k}$ respectively. It therefore follows that $\mathbf{k}$ can also be written in the form $k_i = -\partial\alpha_{ij}/\partial x_j$ where $\alpha_{ij} = \Phi\delta_{ij} - \varepsilon_{ijl}A_l$. From the definitions of Φ and $\mathbf{A}$ it may be seen that, although $\mathbf{k}$ vanishes outside the body, Φ and $\mathbf{A}$ have values Φ' and $\mathbf{A}'$ that are not, in general, zero, so that at exterior points the tensor $\alpha'_{ij} = \Phi'\delta_{ij} - \varepsilon_{ijl}A'_l$ can be non-zero. Now, the surface stress $\mathbf{\Lambda}$ arises precisely because the body force density $g_i = g_i^\dagger - \partial\alpha_{ij}/\partial x_j$ varies rapidly within a thin transition layer at an element $d\mathbf{S}$ of the physical bounding surface of the body. Consider therefore a thin pill-box shaped Gaussian volume element with opposite surfaces normal to $d\mathbf{S}$, of area dS and located just outside and just inside the transition layer. Then, $\Lambda_i\, dS$ is just the integral of g_i over this volume element and this, in turn, is equal, using the Gauss divergence theorem, equation (49a) and

$$g_i = g_i^\dagger - \frac{\partial\alpha_{ij}}{\partial x_j}, \tag{53a}$$

to the difference between the values of $(H_iB_j - \tfrac{1}{2}\mu_0 H^2\delta_{ij} - \alpha_{ij})n_j\, dS$ at the two opposite surfaces. Moreover, the derivation of (48) using (47) shows that this difference is just dS multiplied by

$$\Lambda_i = \Lambda_i^* + (\alpha_{ij} - \alpha'_{ij})n_j. \tag{53b}$$

It may be noted that the use of the Gauss divergence theorem is justified in view of the assumptions made above about the form of $\mathbf{k}$ and $\bar{\mathbf{k}}$. The values of $\mathbf{k}$ and $\bar{\mathbf{k}}$ implied by equations (53) must, of course, be in conformity with equation (51) and since, as noted in 3.4(a), the thin transition layer must be excluded in evaluating the volume integral of $\mathbf{k}$, this imposes the restriction that $\alpha'_{ij}n_j$ must integrate to zero over an exterior closed surface. Similarly, equation (52) imposes a further restriction on integrals involving α'_{ij} over exterior surfaces. Moreover, it is a fact, as suggested by the form of (53b), that $\mathbf{\Lambda} - \mathbf{\Lambda}^*$ is a linear vector function of $\mathbf{n}$. This does not follow immediately† from the fact that k_i, α_{ij} and α'_{ij} are independent of the n_i but it may be readily demonstrated (Birss 1967) by considering the application of (51) to a series of small tetrahedra with the same magnetic conditions at corresponding interior points. Thus, since Λ_i^* is cubic in the n_i, whilst $\mathbf{\Lambda} - \mathbf{\Lambda}^*$ is a linear vector function of $\mathbf{n}$, it follows that the specifically surface stress $\mathbf{\Lambda}$ cannot, in general, be zero.

As long as $\mathbf{k}$ is unknown, then so is α_{ij}. However, in order to satisfy the two requirements, mentioned above, imposed by equations (51) and (52), it is a sufficient but not a necessary requirement that $\alpha'_{ij} = 0$. This means that some, but not all, possible forms of $\mathbf{g}$ and $\mathbf{\Lambda}$ may be written in the form

$$g_i = g_i - \frac{\partial a_{ij}}{\partial x_j}, \tag{54a}$$

$$\Lambda_i = \Lambda_i^* + a_{ij}n_j, \tag{54b}$$

where a_{ij} is a tensor that is completely arbitrary except for the requirement that it must vanish outside S. The utility of equations (54) is associated with the fact that $\mathbf{k}$, and hence α_{ij}, is unknown; it is not, of course, true that the existence of equations (54) is a consequence of the existence of equations (53). By making suitable choices of the form of a_{ij} subject to this requirement it is possible to relate equations (54) to the equivalent pole and current models

† For example, if $\beta_{ij} = H_i B_j - \frac{1}{2}\mu_o H^2 \delta_{ij}$, the interior and exterior values of $\mathbf{H}$ and $\mathbf{B}$ are connected by boundary conditions that depend on $\mathbf{n}$ and, in fact, $(\beta_{ij} - \beta'_{ij})n_j = (I_k n_k)^2 n_i / 2\mu_o$, although both β_{ij} and β'_{ij} are independent of the n_i.

considered in Chapter 2. For example, one possible tensor would be

$$a_{ij} = H_i I_j\,, \tag{55a}$$

and substitution in (54) and comparison with (114) of 2.4 reveals that this choice corresponds to the equivalent pole model. Similarly,

$$a_{ij} = \tfrac{1}{2}\left[\frac{B^2}{\mu_o} - \mu_o H^2\right]\delta_{ij} - \frac{I_i B_j}{\mu_o}\,, \tag{55b}$$

which also vanishes outside the body, corresponds to the equivalent current model used in deriving (116) of 2.4.

Equations (54) and (49) have been derived for the magnetic case: the analogous equations for $\mathbf{g}^e$ and $\mathbf{\Lambda}^e$ may be obtained by replacing μ_o, μ_r and H_i by ε_o, ε_r and E_i respectively.

The existence of the terms involving α_{ij} in (53) is disappointing for it prevents an unambiguous specification of $\mathbf{g}$ and $\mathbf{\Lambda}$. This is unfortunate because there is no doubt about the physical existence of magnetic forces and they have in the past led, for example, to the mechanical failure of apparatus for accelerating atomic particles to high energies. It is also a matter of experience that parts of large rotating electromagnetic machines can snap off under the action of magnetic forces—notwithstanding any ambiguity in their specification! In particular, breakage of interpole bolts and the fatigue failure of laminations in stator teeth may be mentioned. However, the occurrence of α_{ij} in (53) suggests that a critical re-examination of the way in which stress—and particularly magnetic stress—is introduced might be profitable. Such a re-examination is presented in 4.2.

PROBLEMS 3

1. By considering the components of the vector equation $\mathbf{A} = \mathbf{B} \times \mathbf{C}$, verify that it can be written in the form $A_i = \varepsilon_{ijk} B_j C_k$. Hence check that the equation $\phi = \mathbf{A} \cdot \mathbf{B} \times \mathbf{C}$ may be written as $\phi = \varepsilon_{ijk} A_i B_j C_k$.

2. By considering the components of the vector equation $\mathbf{U} = \text{curl}\,\mathbf{V}$, verify that it can be written in the form $U_i = \varepsilon_{ijk}\partial V_k/\partial x_j$. Hence check that Stokes's theorem may be expressed in the form

$$\oint V_i\, dl_i = \iint \varepsilon_{ijk} \frac{\partial V_k}{\partial x_j} n_i\, dS\,.$$

3. Use the fact that the total ponderomotive torque is given by

$$\mathbf{\Gamma} = \iiint_V [\mathbf{L} + \mathbf{r} \times \mathbf{g}]\, dV + \oint\!\!\!\oint_S \mathbf{r} \times \mathbf{\Lambda}\, dS$$

and by the Maxwellian expression

$$\mathbf{\Gamma} = \oint\!\!\!\oint_S \mu_o[(\mathbf{r} \times \mathbf{H}')(\mathbf{H}' . \mathbf{n}) - \tfrac{1}{2}H'^2(\mathbf{r} \times \mathbf{n})]\, dS$$

$$= \oint\!\!\!\oint_S \mu_o[\mu_r(\mathbf{r} \times \mathbf{H})(\mathbf{H} . \mathbf{n}) - \tfrac{1}{2}H^2(\mathbf{r} \times \mathbf{n})]\, dS$$

$$+ \oint\!\!\!\oint_S \tfrac{1}{2}\mu_o(\mu_r - 1)^2(\mathbf{H} . \mathbf{n})^2(\mathbf{r} \times \mathbf{n})\, dS$$

to show that the $\mathbf{k} = \mathbf{g} - \mathbf{g}^\dagger$ and $\bar{\mathbf{k}} = \mathbf{\Lambda} - \mathbf{\Lambda}^*$ of 3.4(c) satisfy the equation

$$\iiint_V [\mathbf{L} + \mathbf{r} \times \mathbf{k}]\, dV + \oint\!\!\!\oint_S \mathbf{r} \times \bar{\mathbf{k}}\, dS = 0 .$$

CHAPTER 4

The Force Distribution

4.1 Microscopic electromagnetic theories

(*a*) *Introduction.* The problem of specifying the distribution of ponderomotive forces in material bodies has in the past been examined far more extensively in connection with magnetic materials than with dielectric materials, and in what follows the discussion will be presented in magnetic terms: dielectric materials will be mentioned only when it is necessary to make a distinction between the two cases.

The most obvious microscopic approach is to start from equation (86) of 2.3(d) for $\bar{\zeta}$. However, although it is possible to average **e** and **b** to obtain $\bar{\mathbf{e}} = \mathbf{E}$ and $\bar{\mathbf{b}} = \mathbf{B}$, it is not possible to adopt a similar procedure to average ζ unless more information is available about the form of the microscopic fields. Moreover, the microscopic fields must be known not only before and after the application of external fields but also as a function of the configuration of the system, since the material may be strained by the joint action of ponderomotive forces and forces provided by mechanical constraints. Finally, it may be noted that even if such a complete specification of the microscopic fields were available, this approach would only be realistic if a completely electromagnetic theory of the constitution of matter were accepted. This extreme position has been adopted, for example, by Mason and Weaver (1929) who supposed that the quantities with which mechanics deals are 'the statistical aspects of an underlying fine-grained electrodynamics', but it is now believed that microscopic interparticle forces are not completely electromagnetic in character.

Another possible microscopic approach to the problem is to represent the macroscopic magnetization of a body as arising from a large number of microscopic dipoles and to evaluate the magnetic force on an individual dipole due to the field, $\mathbf{H}^{\mathrm{dip}}$, of all the other dipoles in the body at the position of the dipole under consideration. If $\mathbf{H}^{o}$ is the applied field—that is the field that would exist in the absence of the body—then, on this view, **g** is determined by the gradient of the effective field, $\mathbf{H}^{\mathrm{eff}} = \mathbf{H}^{o} + \mathbf{H}^{\mathrm{dip}}$, at an individual dipole. The dipoles are usually assumed to be arranged to form some sort of lattice and the evaluation of $\mathbf{H}^{\mathrm{dip}}$ involves a summation over lattice points. The most useful approach is due to Lorentz (1909) but before considering his method it is necessary to examine the macroscopic field inside a magnetized body and to discuss the closely related topic of demagnetizing fields.

(*b*) *Demagnetizing fields.* The determination of the macroscopic magnetic field inside a magnetized body is a classical problem in the theory of magnetostatics and it is best approached by a consideration of the magnetic scalar potential, Ω. If two unlike charges are situated at adjacent points, the electrostatic potential of the pair is given, in an ovious notation, by $4\pi\varepsilon_o\Phi = q/r_2 - q/r_1$. However, over the vector distance $d\mathbf{r}$ separating the two charges, the scalar function r^{-1} changes by $d\mathbf{r}\,.\,\mathrm{grad}\,r^{-1}$, so that $4\pi\varepsilon_o\Phi = -\mathbf{p}\,.\,\mathrm{grad}\,r^{-1}$, where $\mathbf{p} = q\,d\mathbf{r}$ is the dipole moment. The corresponding expression for the magnetic scalar potential of a body of volume V is

$$\Omega^D = -\frac{1}{4\pi\mu_o}\iiint\limits_V I_j\frac{\partial}{\partial x_j}\left(\frac{1}{r}\right)dV. \qquad (1)$$

For points within the body, r^{-1} becomes infinite within the region of integration, and this integral is improper. It must therefore be evaluated by excluding a small region V_o about the interior point, evaluating the integral over the volume $V - V_o$ and then proceeding to the limit as V_o tends to zero. When the singularity in an integrand becomes infinite as r^{-n} then the corresponding integral is convergent for $n < 3$, that is the integral approaches a limit that is independent of the shape of the excluded volume V_o (Leatham 1913). For $n > 3$ the integral is divergent (i.e. the limit is infinite), whilst for $n = 3$ the integral approaches a limit that depends on the shape of the excluded volume and it is therefore said to be semiconvergent. Since $I_j\partial r^{-1}/\partial x_j = -I_j r_j/r^3$ near the singularity, the integral expression (1) is convergent.†

† Confusion is sometimes occasioned by the fact that the integral expression for the field at an interior point—unlike that for the potential—is semiconvergent since it involves a singular integrand of the order (3) of the integration. For example, Brown (1962) comments that 'the field of a continuous volume distribution of dipole sources, at a point of the distribution, is a meaningless concept'

Consider now the case of a homogeneous, isotropic body that is uniformly magnetized, so that **I** does not depend on position within the body. Because (1) is convergent it is permissible to interchange the order of the integration and differentiation to give

$$\Omega^D = -\frac{1}{4\pi\mu_o} I_j \frac{\partial \Xi}{\partial x_j}, \tag{2a}$$

where

$$\Xi = \iiint_V \left(\frac{1}{r}\right) dV. \tag{2b}$$

But Ξ is a quantity familiar in the classical theory of gravitation: it is just the gravitational potential (in suitable units) of a body of volume V and of unit density. The problem of ascertaining the magnetic potential for a uniformly magnetized body is thus mathematically equivalent (as was first discovered by Poisson) to that of determining the gravitational field of a body of the same shape and of uniform density. Now, if the uniform magnetization is produced as a result of placing the body in a field $\mathbf{H}^o$ that was originally uniform, the contribution $\mathbf{H}^D = \mathbf{H} - \mathbf{H}^o$ of the magnetized body to the total field **H** must also be uniform. But

$$\mathbf{H}^D = -\text{grad}\,\Omega^D, \tag{3}$$

so that, if $\mathbf{H}^D$ is uniform throughout the body, Ω^D must be linear in the x_i and Ξ must be a quadratic function of these coordinates.

The only known cases in which Ξ is quadratic in the x_i within the body are those in which the body is bounded by a complete surface of the second degree, and the only case in which such a body is of finite dimensions is when it is an ellipsoid. For example, consider

and suggests that the physical interpretation of this statement is connected with the fact that the form of the elementary dipole has been left undefined and would differ, for example, near an Ampèrian current loop and near two monopoles in close proximity. However, it is clear that this last observation is really a comment on the impossibility of ascertaining the microscopic vector **b** unless the form of the elementary dipole is specified. Within the framework of macroscopic electromagnetic theory, the field at an interior point must be obtained by evaluating the gradient of the convergent integral (1) for the potential: the issue of the convergence of the corresponding expression for the field is irrelevant.

the degenerate case of a spherical body, for which it may readily be shown (Problem 1) that

$$\Xi = 2\pi(a^2 - \tfrac{1}{3}d^2), \tag{4}$$

for an interior point at a distance d from the centre of a sphere of radius a. Thus, for a sphere uniformly magnetized parallel to the x_3-axis,

$$\Omega^D = \frac{Ix_3}{3\mu_o}, \tag{5}$$

since $d^2 = x_i x_i$ and $I = I_3$. It follows from (3) that the field $\mathbf{H}^D$ is also parallel to the x_3 direction and of magnitude $H^D = -I/3\mu_o$. This field is uniform, as expected, so that a uniform magnetization is produced in a spherical body by placing it in a uniform field $\mathbf{H}^o$, the field at interior points being given by

$$\mathbf{H} = \mathbf{H}^o + \mathbf{H}^D = \mathbf{H}^o - \frac{D\mathbf{I}}{\mu_o}, \tag{6}$$

where $D = \frac{1}{3}$. $\mathbf{H}^D$ is referred to as the demagnetizing field and D is known as the demagnetizing factor.

It is interesting to compare this method of obtaining the macroscopic field $\mathbf{H}$ with a purely magnetostatic approach. The magnetic potential Ω^o corresponding to the original field $\mathbf{H}^o$ may, of course, be taken to be just $-H^o x_3$, and the technique is therefore to seek potentials Ω^D and Ω' which satisfy $\nabla^2\Omega = \nabla^2(\Omega^o + \Omega^D) = 0$ inside the sphere and $\nabla^2\Omega' = 0$ outside, satisfy boundary conditions on the potentials and their derivatives at the surface of the sphere and are subject to the requirement that Ω' tends to Ω^o at infinity. Taking the x_3-axis as the polar axis of spherical polar coordinates (r, θ, ϕ), it can readily be shown (Problem 2) that for constant permeability these conditions are satisfied by

$$\begin{aligned} \Omega &= \frac{-3\mu_o}{\mu + 2\mu_o} H^o r \cos\theta, \\ \Omega' &= \frac{\mu - \mu_o}{\mu + 2\mu_o}\frac{a^3}{r^2} H^o \cos\theta - H^o r \cos\theta. \end{aligned} \tag{7}$$

Furthermore, (Problem 2) at points inside the sphere $\mathbf{H} = -\operatorname{grad}\Omega$

and $\mathbf{I} = (\mu - \mu_o)\mathbf{H}$ are both uniform and directed along the x_3-axis, whilst the magnitudes H and I are such that $H = H^o - I/3\mu_o$, in conformity with (6), and

$$\Omega = \frac{Ir\cos\theta}{3\mu_o} - H^o r\cos\theta\,,$$
$$\Omega' = \frac{Ia^3\cos\theta}{3\mu_o r^2} - H^o r\cos\theta, \tag{8}$$

in conformity with (5). Although this derivation assumes a constant permeability, μ, it is clear that it also holds for a material in which μ is a single-valued function of H, since the solution must be unique and the one obtained is one for which μ would be constant everywhere inside the sphere because of the constancy of H.

Reverting now to the situation in which the external surface of the body is not spherical, consider the general case of an ellipsoidal body. Let the centre of the body be at the origin of rectangular Cartesian coordinates x_i that coincide with the principal axes of the ellipsoid, so that the equation of the ellipsoid may be written in the form

$$\frac{x_1^2}{a_1^2} + \frac{x_2^2}{a_2^2} + \frac{x_3^2}{a_3^2} = 1\,. \tag{9}$$

This case is best approached by using Ξ in (2a) to evaluate Ω^D, since a direct magnetostatic solution is a matter of some complexity. For an ellipsoid of unit density, Ξ is well known (Thomson and Tait 1883, Webster 1925, Kellogg 1929) and may be written in the form

$$\Xi = \pi a_1 a_2 a_3 \int_0^\infty \left[1 - \frac{x_1^2}{a_1^2+s} - \frac{x_2^2}{a_2^2+s} - \frac{x_3^2}{a_3^2+s}\right]\frac{ds}{R(s)}, \tag{10a}$$

where

$$R(s) = [(a_1^2+s)(a_2^2+s)(a_3^2+s)]^{\frac{1}{2}}\,, \tag{10b}$$

a form that was first given by Dirichlet. When Ω^D and then $\mathbf{H}^D$ are evaluated from Ξ using (2a) and (3) it is found that

$$H_i^D = -\frac{D_{ij}I_j}{\mu_o}\,, \tag{11}$$

where D_{ij} is the demagnetizing tensor

$$D_{ij} = \frac{a_1 a_2 a_3}{2} \int_0^\infty \frac{ds}{(a_i^2 + s)R(s)} \delta_{ij}. \tag{12}$$

The values of the three components D_{11}, D_{22}, D_{33} of D_{ij} have been given for triaxial ellipsoids by Stoner (1945) and Osborn (1945). Stoner presented his results graphically whilst Osborn gave both graphs and numerical data. In cases not covered by these publications the formulae (12) may be rewritten in terms of normal elliptic integrals of the first and second kinds (Pierce 1929) and the D_{ij} may then be evaluated using standard tables of these integrals. However, it is rarely that ellipsoidal bodies are met with in practice, although ellipsoids of revolution—being much easier to manufacture—are widely used. The remainder of this section is therefore devoted to an evaluation of the demagnetizing factors for prolate and oblate spheroids, and to the introduction of yet another method that can be used to calculate the D_{ij}.

If the substitution $\phi = \mathbf{I} \,.\, \mathbf{n}/r$ is made in equation (17) of 2.1 the relationship

$$\oiint_S \frac{I_j n_j}{r} \, dS = \iiint_V I_j \frac{\partial r^{-1}}{\partial x_j} \, dV + \iiint_V \frac{1}{r} \frac{\partial I_j}{\partial x_j} \, dV \tag{13}$$

is obtained. However, when an ellipsoidal body is placed in a uniform field $\mathbf{H}^o$, the magnetization is also uniform. Thus the second volume integral is zero whilst, from (1), the first is equal to $-4\pi\mu_o\Omega^D$, so that, from (3),

$$H_i^D = -\frac{\partial \Omega^D}{\partial x_i} = \frac{1}{4\pi\mu_o} \oiint_S \frac{\partial r^{-1}}{\partial x_i} I_j n_j \, dS = \oiint_S \frac{(-x_i) I_j n_j \, dS}{4\pi\mu_o r^3}. \tag{14}$$

Since it is known that $\mathbf{H}^D$ is uniform, equation (14) provides an alternative method of calculating the coefficients of the demagnetizing tensor, for at the centre of the ellipsoidal body considered above†

$$\mathbf{H}^D = \oiint_S \frac{-\mathbf{r}\left[I_1 \dfrac{px_1}{a_1^2}\right] dS}{4\pi\mu_o r^3} + \oiint_S \frac{-\mathbf{r}\left[I_2 \dfrac{px_2}{a_2^2}\right] dS}{4\pi\mu_o r^3} + \oiint_S \frac{-\mathbf{r}\left[I_3 \dfrac{px_3}{a_3^2}\right] dS}{4\pi\mu_o r^3}, \quad (15a)$$

where

$$p = \left[\frac{x_1^2}{a_1^4} + \frac{x_2^2}{a_2^4} + \frac{x_3^2}{a_3^4}\right]^{-\frac{1}{2}} \quad (15b)$$

is the length of the perpendicular from the origin to the tangent plane to the ellipsoid at dS. Considering only the *first* integral on the right-hand side of (15a), the x_2- and x_3-components of this integral vanish upon integration over all eight octants. The x_1-component is most readily evaluated by transferring to a coordinate system in which the surface of the body is a coordinate surface—that is, in general, a system of ellipsoidal coordinates. Consider, for example, the degenerate case in which the ellipsoid is an ellipsoid of revolution with the x_3-axis as the axis of rotational symmetry and with $a_3 > a_2 = a_1$. The appropriate coordinates in this case are the prolate spheroidal coordinates ξ, η, ϕ, where

$$\begin{aligned} x_1 &= a \sinh \xi \sin \eta \cos \phi, \\ x_2 &= a \sinh \xi \sin \eta \sin \phi, \\ x_3 &= a \cosh \xi \cos \eta. \end{aligned} \quad (16)$$

The coordinates ξ, η and ϕ can vary within the ranges $0 \leqslant \xi \leqslant \infty$, $0 \leqslant \eta \leqslant \pi$ and $0 \leqslant \phi \leqslant 2\pi$ as indicated in Fig. 4.1, and the constant a is chosen so that the coordinate ξ has a constant value ξ_o over the surface of the body. The equation of the prolate spheroid in the Cartesian coordinates is thus

$$\frac{x_1^2}{a^2 \sinh^2 \xi_o} + \frac{x_2^2}{a^2 \sinh^2 \xi_o} + \frac{x_3^2}{a^2 \cosh^2 \xi_o} = 1, \quad (17)$$

† If (9) is written in the form $f(x_i) = 0$, then $\mathbf{n}$ is in the direction of grad f.

so that

$$a_1 = a_2 = a \sinh \xi_o, \qquad a_3 = a \cosh \xi_o. \tag{18}$$

In these prolate spheroidal coordinates the element of surface dS has the form

$$dS = [a(\sinh^2 \xi_o + \sin^2 \eta)^{\frac{1}{2}}\, d\eta][a \sinh \xi_o \sin \eta \, d\phi]. \tag{19}$$

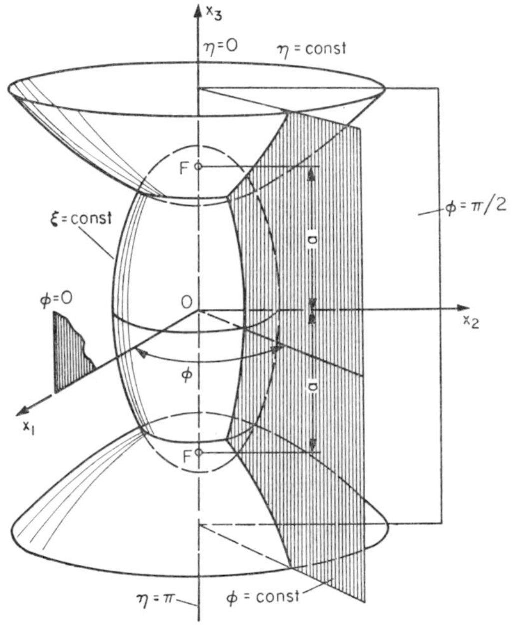

Fig. 4.1. Prolate spheroidal coordinates (ξ, η, ϕ). Coordinate surfaces are prolate spheroids ($\xi =$ const), hyperboloids of revolution ($\eta =$ const), and half-planes ($\phi =$ const).

However, dS and $1/p$ have a common factor, for

$$\begin{aligned} p &= \left[\frac{x_1^2}{a_1^4} + \frac{x_2^2}{a_1^4} + \frac{x_3^2}{a_3^4}\right]^{-\frac{1}{2}} \\ &= \left[\frac{a^2 \sinh^2 \xi_o \sin^2 \eta}{a^4 \sinh^4 \xi_o} + \frac{a^2 \cosh^2 \xi_o \cos^2 \eta}{a^4 \cosh^4 \xi_o}\right]^{-\frac{1}{2}} \\ &= a_1 a_3 (a_3^2 \sin^2 \eta + a_1^2 \cos^2 \eta)^{-\frac{1}{2}}, \end{aligned} \tag{20}$$

whilst

$$dS = (a_1^2 + a^2 \sin^2 \eta)^{\frac{1}{2}} a_1 \sin \eta \, d\eta \, d\phi$$

$$= (a_3^2 \sin^2 \eta + a_1^2 \cos^2 \eta)^{\frac{1}{2}} a_1 \sin \eta \, d\eta \, d\phi, \tag{21}$$

because $a_3^2 - a_1^2 = a^2$. Thus, since

$$r^3 = (x_1^2 + x_2^2 + x_3^2)^{3/2}$$

$$= a^3(\sinh^2 \xi_o \sin^2 \eta + \cosh^2 \xi_o \cos^2 \eta)^{3/2}$$

$$= (a_1^2 \sin^2 \eta + a_3^2 \cos^2 \eta)^{3/2}, \tag{22}$$

the x_1-component of the first integral on the right-hand side of (15a) may be written in the form $-D_{11} I_1/\mu_o$, where

$$D_{11} = \frac{1}{4\pi a_1^2} \int_{\phi=0}^{2\pi} \int_{\eta=0}^{\pi} \frac{a_1^2 \sin^2 \eta \cos^2 \phi}{(a_1^2 \sin^2 \eta + a_3^2 \cos^2 \eta)^{3/2}} a_1^2 a_3 \sin \eta \, d\eta \, d\phi$$

$$= \frac{\pi a_1^2 a_3^2}{4\pi} \int_0^{\pi} \frac{\sin^3 \eta \, d\eta}{(a_1^2 \sin^2 \eta + a_3^2 \cos^2 \eta)^{3/2}}$$

$$= \frac{a_1^2}{4a_3^2} \int_1^{-1} \frac{(\cos^2 \eta - 1)\, d(\cos \eta)}{\left[1 - \dfrac{(a_3^2 - a_1^2)}{a_3^2} \sin^2 \eta\right]^{3/2}}. \tag{23}$$

This last integral may be evaluated by making the substitution

$$\cos \eta = \frac{\sqrt{1-k^2}}{k} \sinh u, \qquad d(\cos \eta) = \frac{\sqrt{1-k^2}}{k} \cosh u \, du,$$

where $k^2 = (a_3^2 - a_1^2)/a_3^2$. Thus

$$D_{11} = \frac{a_1^2}{4a_3^2}\int_1^{-1} \frac{(\cos^2\eta - 1)\, d(\cos\eta)}{[(1-k^2) + k^2\cos^2\eta]^{3/2}}$$

$$= \frac{a_1^2}{4a_3^2}\int_{u_1}^{0} 2\left[\frac{\tanh^2 u}{k^3} - \frac{\operatorname{sech}^2 u}{k(1-k^2)}\right] du$$

$$= \frac{a_1^2}{2a_3^2 k^3(1-k^2)}\int_{u_1}^{0} [(1-k^2) - \operatorname{sech}^2 u]\, du, \quad (25a)$$

where the lower limit is given by

$$u_1 = \sinh^{-1}\frac{k}{\sqrt{1-k^2}}. \quad (25b)$$

But

$$\int_{u_1}^{0} \operatorname{sech}^2 u\, du = -\tanh u_1, \quad (26)$$

and

$$\tanh\left[\sinh^{-1}\frac{k}{\sqrt{1-k^2}}\right] = k, \quad (27)$$

so that

$$D_{11} = \frac{1}{2}\left(\frac{a_1}{a_3}\right)^2\left[\frac{1}{k^2(1-k^2)} - \frac{u_1}{k^3}\right]$$

$$= \frac{1}{2}\frac{1}{k^2}\left[1 - \frac{1-k^2}{k}\sinh^{-1}\frac{k}{\sqrt{1-k^2}}\right]. \quad (28)$$

This formula is often quoted in the form

$$D_{11} = \frac{1}{2}\frac{m}{m^2-1}\left[m - \frac{1}{\sqrt{m^2-1}}\cosh^{-1} m\right], \quad (29a)$$

where m is the axial ratio

$$m = \frac{a_3}{a_1} = \frac{1}{\sqrt{1-k^2}}. \tag{29b}$$

It is not difficult to show (Problem 3) that the same value of D_{11} can also be obtained by starting from equation (12).

In a similar way the x_1- and x_3-components of the second integral on the right-hand side of (15a) integrate to zero and the x_2-component may be written in the form $-D_{22}I_2/\mu_o$. Inspection shows that D_{22} is given by the same expression as that given for D_{11} by (23), so that $D_{22} = D_{11}$—as must indeed be the case from the symmetry of the problem. The third integral on the right-hand side of (15a) reduces in a similar manner (Problem 4) to an x_3-component $-D_{33}I_3/\mu_o$, where

$$D_{33} = \frac{1-k^2}{k^2}\left[\frac{1}{k}\sinh^{-1}\frac{k}{\sqrt{1-k^2}} - 1\right]$$

$$= \frac{1}{m^2-1}\left[\frac{m}{\sqrt{m^2-1}}\cosh^{-1} m - 1\right]. \tag{30}$$

A similar calculation can be made, using oblate spheroidal coordinates, of the factors D_{ij} for an oblate spheroid with $m = a_3/a_1 < 1$, and the formulae corresponding to (29) and (30) are

$$D_{11} = D_{22} = \frac{1}{2(1-m^2)}\left[\frac{m}{\sqrt{1-m^2}}\cos^{-1} m - m^2\right], \tag{31}$$

$$D_{33} = \frac{1}{(1-m^2)}\left[1 - \frac{m}{\sqrt{1-m^2}}\cos^{-1} m\right]. \tag{32}$$

It may be noted, either from (29) and (30) or from (31) and (32), that

$$D_{11} + D_{22} + D_{33} = 1, \tag{33}$$

and this is a general result that also holds for the triaxial ellipsoid. The alternative derivation of equations (29) to (33) inclusive from the corresponding formulae for Ξ is left as an exercise for the reader (Problem 5).

(*c*) *The method of Lorentz*. The field at a point specified by a vector $\mathbf{r}_n$ due to a magnetic dipole of moment $\mathbf{p}_m$ situated at a point specified by the vector $\mathbf{r}_m$ is just

$$\operatorname{grad}\left[\frac{1}{4\pi\mu_o}\mathbf{p}_m \cdot \operatorname{grad} r_{mn}^{-1}\right] = \frac{1}{4\pi\mu_o}\left[-\frac{\mathbf{p}_m}{r_{mn}^3} + 3\frac{(\mathbf{p}_m \cdot \mathbf{r}_{mn})\mathbf{r}_{mn}}{r_{mn}^5}\right], \tag{34}$$

where $\mathbf{r}_{mn} = \mathbf{r}_n - \mathbf{r}_m$ and the summation convention does not, of course, operate over the indices m and n. This microscopic equation may be summed over all dipoles (i.e. over all lattice points or all m) to yield

$$\mathbf{H}^{\text{dip}} = \sum_{m \neq n} \frac{1}{4\pi\mu_o}\left[-\frac{\mathbf{p}_m}{r_{mn}^3} + 3\frac{(\mathbf{p}_m \cdot \mathbf{r}_{mn})\mathbf{r}_{mn}}{r_{mn}^5}\right]. \tag{35}$$

However, the sum in (35) can not be evaluated directly because the contribution of distant dipoles never ceases to be important. Thus, if the summation is performed over successively larger shells of similar shape to that of the specimen, the number of terms in the sum increases as r^3 whilst the summand in (35) decreases only as r^{-3}. The value of the sum therefore depends on the shape of the bounding surface of the specimen, and this dependence can not be removed by allowing the size to tend to infinity. However, this shape dependence is precisely the same effect as occurs in considering the demagnetizing field and it may be conveniently dealt with by the following method which is due to Lorentz (1909).

Lorentz imagined the dipoles to be separated into groups depending on whether their centres were inside or outside a sphere of such a radius R that R is large compared with interatomic distances but small compared with the dimensions of the specimen. The contribution to $\mathbf{H}^{\text{dip}}$ of the dipoles with centres within the sphere of radius R is obtained by direct summation and in what follows it will be denoted by the symbol $\mathbf{H}^{\Sigma}$. The contribution of the other dipoles is calculated by replacing them by a continuous distribution of magnetization within the volume, V', bounded by S, the outer surface of the body and by S_R, the surface of the sphere of radius R. Since the point at which the field is evaluated is not within the distribution of magnetization, the equivalent pole model of 2.4, specified by volume and surface densities $\rho_M^* = -\text{div}\,\mathbf{I}$ and $\kappa_M^* = \mathbf{I}\,.\,\mathbf{n}$, may be used to obtain the relationship

$$\mathbf{H}^{\text{dip}} = \mathbf{H}^{\Sigma} + \oiint_S \frac{(-\mathbf{r})(\mathbf{I}\,.\,\mathbf{n})\,dS}{4\pi\mu_o r^3}$$

$$+ \oiint_{S_R} \frac{(-\mathbf{r})(\mathbf{I}\,.\,\mathbf{n})\,dS}{4\pi\mu_o r^3} + \iiint_{V'} \frac{(-\mathbf{r})(-\,\text{div}\,\mathbf{I})\,dV}{4\pi\mu_o r^3}. \tag{36}$$

For an array of parallel dipoles, the macroscopic magnetization, $\mathbf{I}$, is solenoidal (or circuital), so that the volume integral vanishes in (36). Moreover, from (14) the surface integral over S is just the demagnetizing field $\mathbf{H}^D$, so that the effective field $\mathbf{H}^{\text{eff}}$ is related to the field $\mathbf{H}^o$ that exists in the absence of the dipoles by

$$\mathbf{H}^{\text{eff}} = \mathbf{H}^o + \mathbf{H}^{\text{dip}} = \mathbf{H}^o + \mathbf{H}^D + \mathbf{H}^L + \mathbf{H}^{\Sigma} = \mathbf{H} + \mathbf{H}^L + \mathbf{H}^{\Sigma}, \tag{37}$$

where the Lorentz field $\mathbf{H}^L$ is given by

$$\mathbf{H}^L = \oiint_{S_R} \frac{(-\mathbf{r})(\mathbf{I}\,.\,\mathbf{n})\,dS}{4\pi\mu_o r^3}. \tag{38}$$

Thus the dependence of $\mathbf{H}^{\text{dip}}$ on the external shape of the body is completely allowed for by the effect of the demagnetizing field in altering $\mathbf{H}^o$ to $\mathbf{H}$.

Since the sphere S_R is centred on the internal point at which $\mathbf{H}^{\text{eff}}$ is to be evaluated, the integral (38) may be evaluated without difficulty. Alternatively, it may be observed by comparison with (14) that $-\mathbf{H}^L$ is just the demagnetizing field for a spherical specimen, so that

$$\mathbf{H}^L = \frac{\mathbf{I}}{3\mu_o}, \tag{39}$$

the change in sign arising from the difference between the sense of the normals to S and S_R.

To evaluate $\mathbf{H}^{\Sigma}$, Lorentz considered the case of an array of equal and parallel dipoles arranged on a cubic lattice. If the components of the vector $-\mathbf{r}_{mn}$ are denoted by x_i then, from equation (35),

$$H_1^{\Sigma} = \frac{1}{4\pi\mu_o}\left[p_1 {\sum}' \frac{r^2 - 3x_1^2}{r^5} - p_2 {\sum}' \frac{3x_1 x_2}{r^5} - p_3 {\sum}' \frac{3x_1 x_3}{r^5}\right], \tag{40}$$

where $r^2 = x_i x_i$ and the primes indicate summation over all lattice points within the sphere S_R except the point at $x_i = 0$. If the summations are performed over successive spherical shells of dipoles centred on the selected one, the constant factor $1/r^5$ may be removed from the summations so that, from symmetry,

$$\begin{gathered}\sum{}' x_1^2 = \sum{}' x_2^2 = \sum{}' x_3^2 = \tfrac{1}{3}\sum{}' r^2, \\ \sum{}' x_1 x_2 = \sum{}' x_2 x_3 = \sum{}' x_3 x_1 = 0.\end{gathered} \tag{41}$$

Each of the three sums in (40) therefore vanishes so that $H_1^\Sigma = 0$ and, similarly, $H_2^\Sigma = H_3^\Sigma = 0$. The contribution of the dipoles inside the sphere of radius R to $\mathbf{H}^\Sigma$—and therefore to $\mathbf{H}^{\text{eff}}$—is thus zero. Hence

$$\mathbf{H}^{\text{eff}} = \mathbf{H} + \frac{\mathbf{I}}{3\mu_o}, \tag{42}$$

for the cubic array, and the same result is obtained for a random distribution of equal and parallel dipoles. In view of the remarks made in 4.2(b) about evaluating improper integrals by proceeding to the limit as a small excluded volume V_o tends to zero it may, perhaps, be asked why the term $\mathbf{I}/3\mu_o$ does not enter into the expression for $\mathbf{H}$ as well as into (42) for $\mathbf{H}^{\text{eff}}$. However, in evaluating the gradient of Ω, its values at two adjacent points are considered so that if V_o is bounded by a spherical surface then two spheres are involved. Effectively, therefore, a sphere bounding V_o would move with the internal point whilst the external boundary of the body does not.

(*d*) *The applicability of the Lorentz method.* A fundamental disadvantage of the Lorentz method is that, although it readily provides a value for $\mathbf{H}^{\text{eff}}$, it does not lend itself to the calculation of grad $\mathbf{H}^{\text{eff}}$ and hence to the evaluation of the body force density $\mathbf{g}$. However, the method involves a model and before proceeding further it is desirable to ask how successful is the method in predicting, for actual materials, the effective field itself? This question has been considered extensively in the analogous problem of calculating the effective electric field acting on a dipole in a dielectric in order that the observed permittivity may be explained in terms of the polarizabilities of individual molecules.

The model involves an array of point dipoles in fixed positions and all parallel to each other, the interaction between them corresponding to the classical expression (35). There is no doubt that (42) gives the formally correct result for such a model but, in considering actual dielectric and magnetic materials, all the features of the model are in turn open to criticism. The assumption that all the dipoles are parallel is most realistic for dielectric materials in which the polarization is distortional (e.g. ionic) and is therefore due to charges being separated by the field. However, in this case, far from being point dipoles, the dipoles are of finite size equal essentially to the ionic spacing and each ion is subject to a field that is far from uniform. The resulting induced quadrupole and higher-order electric moments in turn produce fields at neighbouring ions which affect their dipole moments and therefore the observed polarization. An extreme form of ionic polarization is exhibited by certain compounds, such as Rochelle salt, potassium dihydrogen phosphate and barium titanate, which are ferroelectric, that is they are spontaneously polarized in the absence of an applied field. Here the polarization and hence the ionic displacement is large, and it is therefore important that the effective electric field be calculated at displaced positions in the lattice. This information is not provided by the Lorentz method, although some progress has been made in such calculations by Slater (1950) and by Jaynes (1953).

For dielectric materials in which the polarization is orientational (i.e. due to the existence of permanent molecular dipole moments), the assumption that all the dipoles are parallel is vitiated by the effect of thermal agitation. Indeed, if thermal agitation were absent, the dipoles would all be aligned parallel by an infinitesimally small field,† and it is impossible to treat orientational polarization correctly without considering the statistical problem of thermal agitation. There are two effects to consider here (Jaynes 1953). First, if a particular dipole is rotated by an angle θ whilst the rest are held parallel, then its contribution to the polarization is proportional to $\cos\theta$, a spherical harmonic of first order, whilst each component of its contribution to the field acting on a second dipole varies according to a spherical harmonic of second order. Therefore there is not, in general, the same relation between the contribution of a dipole to the polarization and its contribution to the field at other dipoles. This effect exists for dipoles at any separation, and the Lorentz field

† This is the 'polarizability catastrophe' (Kittel 1956).

will be correct only when certain conditions are imposed on the symmetry of the spatial and angular distributions of the dipoles. The second effect arises because the angular orientations of dipoles that are close together are strongly correlated. In other words the rotation of the first dipole would, in fact, tend to rotate its neighbours out of their initial orientations and the result of this local distortion of the pattern is to alter the field acting on the first dipole. This correlation effect has been taken into account in an approximate fashion by Onsager (1936) who imagined the surrounding dipoles to be replaced by a homogeneous dielectric material. The dipole under consideration is supposed to be located in a spherical cavity excavated in this material, but the dipole itself is replaced by a uniformly and permanently polarized sphere that can rotate freely. It is clear, however, that Onsager's model is such an extreme idealisation of the actual physical situation that it is very difficult to determine the conditions for its validity.

The assumption that all the dipoles are parallel is more realistic for ferromagnetic materials than for dielectrics because of the existence of strong exchange forces. These are forces, of quantum-mechanical origin, that tend to produce parallelism of electron spins without any reference to the orientation of the spins relative to the lattice. The isotropic exchange interaction between neighbouring dipoles is far stronger than the classical magnetic dipole-dipole interaction assumed in the method of Lorentz, as evidenced by the fact that the effective field, $\mathbf{H}^{\text{eff}}$, is given not by (42) but by $\mathbf{H} + q\mathbf{I}$ where q is the extremely large Weiss intramolecular field constant (Bozorth 1951). It is nevertheless reasonable to examine whether the classical dipole-dipole forces might be the origin of anisotropic properties of ferromagnetic single crystals such as, for example, the observed spontaneous magnetostrictive strain. According to the model used in the Lorentz method the energy of a single dipole is given by

$$-\mathbf{p}.\mathbf{H}^{\text{eff}} = -\mathbf{p}.(\mathbf{H}^{o} + \mathbf{H}^{D} + \mathbf{H}^{L} + \mathbf{H}^{\Sigma}). \tag{43}$$

Of course, $\mathbf{H}^{\Sigma}$ is zero for an exactly cubic lattice, but if the lattice is uniformly strained then x_i may be replaced in (40) by $x_i + E_{ij}x_j$ and $r^2 = x_ix_i$ by $r^2 + E_{ij}x_ix_j$, where E_{ij} is the symmetrical strain tensor. The term $\mathbf{p} . \mathbf{H}^{\Sigma}$ is then no longer zero and Powell (1931) has used (43) to derive an energy density that depends on demagnetizing factors, their strain dependence and lattice sums performed over the (strained) sphere S_R. The dependence of the lattice sums on strain permits a calculation of the spontaneous magnetostriction whilst the occurrence of the strain dependence of the demagnetizing factors leads to the prediction of specific expressions for the form effect, i.e. the dependence of magnetic deformation on the shape of the body. These expressions are incorrect, for reasons that are indicated subsequently, but the important fact to note is that the calculations of magnetostriction give values that are much too small to be reconciled with experimental observations.† Hence, even the anisotropic part of the interaction between dipoles cannot be dealt with by the assumption in the method of Lorentz of classical dipole-dipole coupling. Furthermore, the assumption of parallel dipoles implies that, for ferromagnetics, the Lorentz method can only be applied to regions that are magnetized to saturation.

In summary, therefore, it may be said that the extent of current activity in the microscopic theory of dielectrics and ferroelectrics is indicative of the inapplicability of the Lorentz and related methods, whilst, for ferromagnetics, attempts are no longer made to explain effective fields in classical terms. It is thus desirable to examine whether the problem of specifying the distribution of ponderomotive forces in material bodies can be approached from a macroscopic viewpoint.

4.2 Macroscopic theories

(*a*) *Introduction.* In a macroscopic theory the solid material is regarded as a continuum and an attempt is made to formulate the problem in terms of macroscopic quantities, such as the applied field and the stress tensor. In 3.4 it was assumed that the forces operating in, for example, a magnetic material can be satisfactorily described by means of a specifically magnetic body force density **g** and a specifically magnetic stress vector **m**. In reality, however, the forces acting are forces between particles (e.g. molecules) and between field and particles, so that, as pointed out by Poincaré (1892), it is not obvious that this assumption is valid. For example, if the body

† This approach also predicts (incorrectly) that the magnetocrystalline anisotropy constants will be zero.

force $\mathbf{g}dV$ were to depend on the *shape* of the volume element dV, a formulation in terms of $\mathbf{g}$ and $\mathbf{m}$ would be unacceptable.

In authoritative works on continuum mechanics, stress is introduced by means of the stress hypothesis of Euler and Cauchy (Truesdell and Toupin 1960), that is by asserting that acting upon any imagined closed geometrical surface σ within the body there exists a field of stress vectors, $\mathbf{t} + \mathbf{m}$, which has an equivalent effect to the (interparticle) forces exerted by the material outside σ upon the material within. The possibility of the interparticle forces contributing to $\mathbf{g}$ is thus specifically excluded. When an ordinary elastic body is deformed by extrinsic forces, the arrangement of molecules within the body is altered and internal forces are brought into play which are, in reality, forces of interaction between molecules. That they can be represented in a continuum theory by means of a stress vector $\mathbf{t}$ is a consequence of the fact that intermolecular forces have a very short range of action; their effect extends only over distances of the same order as the distances between molecules, whereas in the theory of elasticity—which is a macroscopic, continuum theory—the only distances considered are those that are large compared with intermolecular distances. Thus in the theory of elasticity the range of action of the intermolecular forces can be taken to be effectively zero: in other words the interparticle forces, which are dealt with by the introduction of the stress vector $\mathbf{t}$, are, as regards a continuum theory, short-range forces which act only between neighbouring points. It is for this reason that the force exerted on a volume element by the rest of the body may be considered to act only by way of stresses, $\mathbf{t}$ exerted across the surface of the volume element.

In a magnetic body the situation is rather different because the interparticle forces are partly magnetic in origin since the molecules possess a magnetic moment. Furthermore, the magnetic interparticle forces are partly of short-range character (e.g. exchange forces) and partly of long-range character (e.g. classical magnetic dipole-dipole forces). Cauchy's stress hypothesis cannot therefore be retained without modification since the long-range forces cannot be satisfactorily accommodated in the stress vector $\mathbf{m}$. As it stands Cauchy's hypothesis implies that $\mathbf{g} = \mu_o \mathbf{J} \times \mathbf{H}^o + \mathbf{I} . \nabla \mathbf{H}^o$; but it is known that one macroscopic effect of the interparticle interactions is to modify $\mathbf{H}^o$ to $\mathbf{H}$, so that some modification in $\mathbf{g}$ is also to be expected. It is therefore necessary to conclude that the interparticle forces must contribute to **g** as well as **m**. It is not suggested that the modification of $\mathbf{H}^o$ to **H** is accompanied by a modification of **g** to $\mu_o \mathbf{J} \times \mathbf{H} + \mathbf{I} . \nabla \mathbf{H}$, for the body force density is a product of second order in the electromagnetic vectors and, in proceeding by averaging from the microscopic vectors **j** and **b** to the macroscopic vectors **J**, **H** and **I**, the average of a product of two functions is not, in general, equal to the product of their individual average values. However, some modification of **g** is clearly necessary. It will therefore be assumed that a formulation in terms of **g** and **m** may be retained but that Cauchy's stress hypothesis must be modified to permit the interparticle interactions to contribute to **g** as well as to **m**. This is the minimum alteration that can be made and it can, in the last analysis, only be justified by the application of Ockham's razor, which, as restated by Newton (1687), requires that: 'We are to admit no more causes of natural things than such as are both true and sufficient to explain their appearances, for nature is simple and affects not the pomp of superfluous causes.'

The vectors **g** and **m** may be acceptable but, again as pointed out by Poincaré (1892), they may still not be unique, that is the partition of the total force density $g_i + \partial m_{ij}/\partial x_j$ between its two constituent terms may not be unique. In ordinary elasticity the correct stress is obtained only if all the contributions to the body force density are correctly recognised. Moreover it is to prevent the explicit specification of the intrinsic (interparticle) forces that the stress vector is introduced. It is therefore to be expected that allowing interparticle forces to contribute to **g** as well as to **m** may lead to ambiguity. Indeed the uncertainty over the interparticle contributions to **g** (or **m**) has led in the past to a considerable measure of controversy. Further controversy has arisen because of a failure to recognise that the surface σ mentioned in the Cauchy hypothesis is an imagined geometrical surface, not a physical surface obtained by making an internal cut in the material. This failure leads, as shown by Slepian (1950), to erroneous conclusions about the form of the stress tensor—and this will be considered further in 4.2(b). Nevertheless, it might be thought that the short-range magnetic forces could be taken into account by an alteration in the stress vector whilst the long-range magnetic force could be absorbed into the body force. Unfortunately, however, long-range interparticle forces act also at short distances and no such unique separation is possible since some of the particles between which these forces act *are* separated by short distances. This situation may be contrasted with the familiar one of an elastic body subject to the gravitational field of the earth. Gravitational forces are long-range forces that also act at short distances, but here no two parts of the body and the earth respectively are separated by distances of microscopic dimensions. Hence it is possible to focus attention on a limited part of the system, namely the body, and the familiar formulation in terms of a gravitational body force density is satisfactory. This is not, of course, true if the self-gravitational forces between particles in the body are taken into account, but it will be recalled that a consideration of these forces is usually specifically excluded.

As far as experimental observations are concerned, it is clear that no kinematic observation will provide information on how the total force density $g_i + \partial m_{ij}/\partial x_j$ is partitioned into its two constituent terms, for the rate of change of momentum of the particles contained in any volume element is determined by the sum and not by either term separately. The basic problem therefore is to predict **g** and this will be considered further below. It may be noted, however, that the equivalence referred to in the Cauchy hypothesis is an equivalence of forces and not an equivalence in respect of deformation—indeed the strain can only be determined by appending a constitutive relationship. Since kinematic observations fail to specify the stress, it is desirable to enquire whether this specification can be effected by considering the deformation of the body, for in ordinary elasticity the strain depends on the stress and not directly on the body force density. In this connection it is also necessary to enquire whether a formulation in terms of **g** and **m** is *sufficient* to explain the observed deformation or whether it is necessary to introduce, in addition, the idea of a spontaneous strain.

The simplest example of a spontaneous strain is free thermal expansion: in the absence of extrinsic forces a change in the temperature of a body produces a strain $E_{ij} = E\delta_{ij}$ due to thermal expansion and the conventional interpretation is, of course, that the equilibrium state—relative to which strains should be measured—has been altered, so creating a spontaneous strain $E\delta_{ij}$. If the solid body is regarded as a collection of particles, then thermal expansion corresponds to an alteration in the equilibrium position of the particles. However, an ordinary mechanical situation in which deformation is produced by extrinsic forces also corresponds to an alteration in the equilibrium position of the particles (since they must be in equilibrium after deformation). Both the thermal and the mechanical situations can be described in terms of the forces acting on the particles and a difference in formulation only becomes necessary when a change of viewpoint is made and the solid body is regarded as a continuum. This change is accompanied in the mechanical situation, by the introduction of the stress tensor and by the idea that the elastic response of the medium is of a local character, i.e. that the strain is determined by the stress at the same point. Again, in the thermal situation, the strain $E\delta_{ij}$ could be explained by postulating the existence of a specifically thermal stress tensor $\theta_{ij} = YE\delta_{ij}/(1 - 2\nu)$, but this is rejected because there exists a satisfactory theory of thermal expansion, as a volume strain, which deals not with just one material but which relates the observed expansivity of different materials to their individual atomic or molecular constitutions. Of course, the correct prediction of strain at a point does not dictate whether this strain is spontaneous or produced through the operation of stress: however, a further consequence of the theory is that there is no specifically thermal surface stress $\mathbf{T}'$ acting at the bounding surface of the body. Since a constant θ_{ij} could only be maintained† by the operation of a surface stress $\mathbf{T}' = YE\mathbf{n}/(1 - 2\nu)$, this indicates that $\theta_{ij} = 0$ and that free thermal expansion should be classified as a spontaneous strain, E_{ij}^o, the body being regarded as a continuum. It should be noted that in order to make the choice‡ between θ_{ij} and E_{ij}^o it has been necessary to go outside the framework of continuum mechanics. However, the result ($\theta_{ij} = 0$) is precisely that used in thermo-elasticity where it is assumed (Sokolnikoff 1956) that the total strain at a point is the sum of the strain produced by thermal expansion and the elastic strain. Within the framework of continuum mechanics, this result can only be obtained by hypothesis (i.e. the Duhamel-Neumann hypothesis).

† Within the framework of continuum mechanics, stresses describe the equilibrating mechanical response of the material to extrinsic forces: hence a spontaneous *stress* cannot exist.

‡ The basic reason for the difficulty in making this choice is that, although the material is not, in fact, a continuum in a state of stress, this concept is nevertheless used in describing how the extrinsic forces are equilibrated by the interparticle forces.

The analogy between a change in temperature and the application of, for example, a magnetic field resides in the fact that, in principle, the field can also alter the interparticle interactions since the particles carry a magnetic moment. In the presence of ponderomotive forces it may therefore be argued that part of the deformation corresponds to a spontaneous strain E_{ij}^o (as is assumed in standard magnetostriction theory). However, it was shown in 3.4(c) that $\mathbf{\Lambda} \neq 0$ and hence it follows from (42) of 3.4(a) that it is not possible to assume that $m_{ij} = 0$ in this case. It is therefore necessary to formulate the problem in terms of **g**, **m** (or m_{ij}) and E_{ij}^o, and a further difference from the thermal situation arises because $\mathbf{\Lambda}$, and therefore **m**, is non-zero. Since $\theta_{ij} = 0$ experiments on free thermal expansion serve to determine E_{ij}^o but, since $m_{ij} \neq 0$, any stress/strain relationship that may be observed experimentally does not immediately serve to determine m_{ij} or E_{ij}^o because it is not known how much of the deformation is directly attributable to stress and how much to a spontaneous strain. It is possible, however, that the determination of **g**, m_{ij} and E_{ij}^o might be approached in the same way as was the determination of θ_{ij} in the thermal situation, that is by considering what values are called for theoretically, a theory† being judged by the extent to which the observed macroscopic behaviour of different materials is successfully related to their known atomic or molecular properties.

(*b*) *The operational 'definition' of stress.* In a non-magnetic (or non-electrical) body the stress tensor t_{ij} may be operationally defined by imagining that a physical cut is made in the material along an internal element of surface $d\boldsymbol{\sigma} = \mathbf{n}\, d\sigma$. If means are then introduced for keeping the strains in the material on both sides of the cut the same as they were before the cut was made, then the force introduced by these means has components $t_{ij}n_j\, d\sigma$. Since the orientation of $d\boldsymbol{\sigma}$ can be chosen at will, the tensor t_{ij} can, in principle, be operationally defined in this way. It is then possible to use this knowledge of t_{ij} to determine the body force density **f** from equations (35) of 3.3 and to determine the surface stress **T** (or check its correctness) from equations (36).

† The importance of such theories may perhaps be appreciated by realising that, in the absence of temperature as a concept, and therefore of any theory of thermal expansion, thermo-elastic data might well be interpreted in terms of a surface stress $\mathbf{\Theta}$ of unknown origin.

Now, consider the corresponding magnetic case, in which the material is cut along σ or, more precisely, in which a thin shell of material coincident with σ is removed. An interior volume τ is now physically isolated by a thin shell of empty space coincident with the closed surface σ. The force, $\mathbf{F}^p$, on this physically isolated volume is given by (46) of 3.4 with $\mathbf{H}'$ replaced by the field within the cut or, equivalently, by (48) of 3.4 with $\mathbf{H}$ replaced by the field within the material and immediately adjacent to the inner surface of the cut. However, for a very thin shell, this last field is just the field, $\mathbf{H}$, within the uncut material at the geometrical surface σ, so that

$$F_i^p = \iiint_\tau g_i^\dagger \, d\tau + \oint\!\!\oint_\sigma \Lambda_i^* d\sigma, \tag{44a}$$

where $g_i^\dagger$ and Λ_i^* are given by (49) of 3.4. If a similar procedure to that discussed above could be used in the magnetic case to obtain an operationally defined stress tensor m_{ij}^{op}, then the integral of $m_{ij}^{op} n_j \, d\sigma$ over the surface σ would be equal to the expression for F_i^p given by (44a). This is clearly impossible for arbitrary σ since $m_{ij}^{op} n_j$ is linear in the n_i whilst (44a) may be expressed as a surface integral which contains terms that are both linear and cubic in the n_i. However, this difficulty can be concealed by considering a volume element, $d\tau$, in the shape of a rectangular parallelepiped with faces perpendicular to the Cartesian coordinate axes, x_i. The n_i are then either zero or unity, so that the force $d\mathbf{F}^{p'}$ on this element is given by

$$dF_i^{p'} = \left[g_i^\dagger + \frac{1}{2\mu_o} \delta_{ij} \frac{\partial}{\partial x_i} (I_j)^2 \right] d\tau, \tag{44b}$$

and Carpenter (1959) has stated this result (for example, his equation (13) for constant μ_r and div $\mathbf{B} \neq 0$). It is not possible to determine m_{ij}^{op} directly from (44b) for it is not known how much of $d\mathbf{F}^{p'}$ originates as a body force density and how much is transmitted across the surface σ as a stress. Specific expressions for the corresponding stress vector $\mathbf{m}^{op}$ have, however, been obtained by considering the equivalent pole and current models introduced in Chapter 2. It will be recalled that it was shown in 2.4 that in the absence of extrinsic currents a magnetic body is equivalent as far as the magnetic field at exterior and interior points is concerned, to a surface distribution of polarity of density $\kappa_M^* = \mathbf{I} \cdot \mathbf{n}$ and a volume distribution of density

$\rho_M^* = -\operatorname{div} \mathbf{I}$. Thus, for a model in which $\mathbf{J} = 0$ and the actual material is replaced by the distributions κ_M^* and ρ_M^*, equation (110) of 2.4 may be used to show that the 'stress', $\mathbf{m}^{op}(n_1=1)$ corresponding to the face normal to x_1 has the components

$$
\begin{aligned}
m_1^{op}(n_1=1) &= \kappa_M^*\left[\mathbf{H}+\frac{\kappa_M^*}{2\mu_o}\mathbf{n}\right]_1 = I_1H_1+\frac{1}{2\mu_o}I_1^2,\\
m_2^{op}(n_1=1) &= \kappa_M^*\left[\mathbf{H}+\frac{\kappa_M^*}{2\mu_o}\mathbf{n}\right]_2 = I_1H_2,\\
m_3^{op}(n_1=1) &= \kappa_M^*\left[\mathbf{H}+\frac{\kappa_M^*}{2\mu_o}\mathbf{n}\right]_3 = I_1H_3.
\end{aligned}
\tag{45a}
$$

In a similar way the equivalent current model (in which **B** is everywhere reproduced) may be used to obtain (Problem 6) the results

$$
\begin{aligned}
m_1^{op}(n_1=1) &= \frac{1}{\mu_o}\left[I_2B_2+I_3B_3-\tfrac{1}{2}(I_2^2+I_3^2)\right],\\
m_2^{op}(n_1=1) &= -\frac{1}{\mu_o}I_2B_1,\\
m_3^{op}(n_1=1) &= -\frac{1}{\mu_o}I_3B_1,
\end{aligned}
\tag{45b}
$$

and both (45a) and (45b) have been quoted by Brown (1951).

According to the present approach to the problem, $m_{ij}n_j$ is the stress acting across a *geometrical* interior surface and not across a physical surface of separation. It is therefore fundamentally incorrect to introduce a physical cut in order to calculate the force on an element of the uncut material, since a surface stress $\mathbf{\Lambda}$ is introduced thereby which—as demonstrated in 3.4(c)—is non-zero and must certainly contain the cubic term $\mathbf{\Lambda}^*$. Nor is this difficulty removed by proceeding to the limit as the cut thickness tends to zero: it is true that the fields in the material adjacent to the cut tend to their actual values in this mathematical process, but the contribution $\mathbf{\Lambda}^*$ to the stress vector remains, whereas it would disappear in the corresponding physical process of rejoining the material to remove the physical discontinuity. The actual stress can not be equated to the operationally 'defined' stress either in the material or, as is shown below, in either model. For an ordinary elastic material the stress acting at a physical surface of separation is zero: the stress vector that must be introduced to maintain mechanical conditions is thus $m_i = m_{ij}n_j$ and an operational definition of stress is possible. In the magnetic case the stress acting at a physical surface of separation is $\mathbf{\Lambda}$ and the stress that must be introduced to maintan mechanical conditions is therefore $m_i^{op} = m_{ij}n_j - \Lambda_i$. This reveals that equations (45) are appropriate only when $\mathbf{m} = 0$ in the model—in conformity with the absence of any specification of the means whereby the positions of the pole or current distributions are stabilized.

Since $\mathbf{\Lambda}$ is, as indicated in 3.4, both non-zero and unknown (because α_{ij} is unknown) no operational definition of stress is possible. If this fact is ignored and $\mathbf{m}^{op} = \mathbf{m} - \mathbf{\Lambda}$ is identified with $\mathbf{m}$, then the presence in Λ_i of terms that are cubic in the n_i results in two related, but unfortunate, consequences. The first is that the force on a volume element depends on its shape,† so that a volume element on which no force acts can be divided into two parts on each of which a force acts. This is concealed in deriving (44b) by the use of a particular type of volume element: it can also be concealed by always taking (Hammond 1966) volume elements bounded by surfaces parallel or normal to $\mathbf{I}$. The second unfortunate consequence is that $\mathbf{m}$ is not derivable from a tensor, which is another way of saying that it is not a linear vector function of $\mathbf{n}$. The impossibility of expressing m_i^{op} in the form $m_{ij}^{op}n_j$—despite the existence of equations such as (45a) and (45b)—has already been noted. The importance of this is that it means that it is impossible for an arbitrary tetrahedrally shaped volume to be in equilibrium under the action of the corresponding set of (four) stress vectors as its volume tends to zero. The introduction of a cut to effect a physical separation has therefore altered the equilibrium conditions, for the volume must be in equilibrium before the cut is introduced. However, if the statement that the material is in a state of stress has any meaning, then this state of stress must be one in which internal volume elements of any shape and size can be held in equilibrium. In this sense the use of a continuum theory of elasticity *necessitates* the introduction of a stress vector which is a linear vector function of $\mathbf{n}$.

† Furthermore, this would imply, if a distinction is made between 'magnetic' and 'elastic' forces, that in equilibrium the 'elastic' forces must also be shape dependent.

The relationship $\mathbf{m}^{op} = \mathbf{m} - \mathbf{\Lambda}$ holds for the actual material as well as for the model, and it may therefore be seen from the foregoing that it is pointless to try to investigate the form of m_{ij} by performing experiments in which part of a material body is separated from the remainder, because the force on the separated part includes a contribution from the surface of separation which prevents the discovery of what the force on the part would have been had the separation not been made.

It may also be noted that the pole and current models do not reproduce correctly both **H** and **B** at interior points. There is therefore no reason to expect that the stress in the actual material will be the same as the stress in the model. This is confirmed by the fact that the body force density **g** is different for the two models and that an infinite number of values for **g** can be obtained by considering models in which distributions of poles and of currents are combined in appropriate ratios. Nevertheless, the difference in **g** between the pole and current models is not—as is sometimes suggested—due in turn to the difficulty of differentiating between long-range and short-range forces. In both models the intrinsic (e.g. inter-pole) forces contribute to **g** but not to **m**. However, the unambiguous allocation of these forces to the body force density is an artifact of the model. In the actual material the force between two adjacent atoms can always be regarded, wholly or in part, as a surface stress acting across a surface separating them; but from two adjacent regions in a continuous distribution of, for example, polarity there can be successively subtracted without limit regions which are not adjacent and which, therefore, do not interact via a surface stress.

It may be seen from the foregoing that the operational 'definition' of stress cannot be used either as a theoretical concept or as a practical procedure. Although the force on a geometrically demarcated volume can be given a meaning as the force on all the particles contained in the volume, it might be thought that an operational definition would be more satisfactory. Indeed, a familiar presentation of scientific topics is in terms of an operational system in which basic quantities that are susceptible of direct measurement are connected by laws which are to be tested by experiment. This idea is attractive in a pedagogical treatment but its limitations are well-known and have been stated by Southwell (1929). Briefly, the objection is that it rests on a circular argument, for no experiment can be interpreted without recourse to ideas in themselves part of the theory under examination.† The operational 'definition' of stress discussed above will therefore be rejected and, in what follows, the stress vector will be identified with the stress acting over an imaginary geometrical surface. This identification is made in the macroscopic theory associated with the name of Helmholtz.

(*c*) *The theory of Helmholtz.* The basis of the Helmholtz method is to consider the variation in the energy of a body when it is subject to an arbitrary virtual displacement **s** assuming that this energy may be obtained by spatial integration of an energy density w, which may be taken to be $w = \frac{1}{2}\mu H^2$ when the permeability, μ, is constant. As is well known, there is an inherent ambiguity in this expression for w: for example, Stratton (1941) comments

> 'The form of these integrals suggests, but does not prove, the hypothesis that electric and magnetic energies are distributed throughout the field with volume densities respectively,
>
> $$u = \int_0^{\mathbf{D}} \mathbf{E}.d\mathbf{D}, \qquad w = \int_0^{\mathbf{B}} \mathbf{H}.d\mathbf{B}. \tag{46}$$
>
> The derivation of these results was based on the assumption of *reversible* changes.'

In most textbook reproductions of the Helmholtz theory, energy integrals are employed rather than energy densities. A typical treatment is that of Stratton (1941) who obtains the result

$$g_i^e = \rho E_i - \tfrac{1}{2}E^2\frac{\partial \varepsilon}{\partial x_i} + \tfrac{1}{2}\frac{\partial}{\partial x_i}\left[E^2\tau\frac{\partial \varepsilon}{\partial \tau}\right], \tag{47a}$$

for a dielectric fluid of density τ that exhibits a linear relationship between **D** and **E**, the corresponding magnetic result being

$$g_i^m = \varepsilon_{ijk}J_jB_k - \tfrac{1}{2}H^2\frac{\partial \mu}{\partial x_i} + \tfrac{1}{2}\frac{\partial}{\partial x_i}\left[H^2\tau\frac{\partial \mu}{\partial \tau}\right]. \tag{47b}$$

The procedure is to consider the change δW in W, the integral of w over all space, accompanying the virtual displacement **s**, and to

† It is not entirely irrelevant to remark in this connection that experiments in which stresses are measured operationally are performed so infrequently that they practically qualify as gedanken experiments.

manipulate δW into the form of an integral of the scalar product of **s** with some vector function. This function may then be identified with $-\mathbf{g}$ provided $-\delta W$ is also the integral of $\mathbf{g}\,.\,\mathbf{s}$ and **s** is arbitrary. Thus, in (47a), the second term is associated with the fact that a displacement **s** is accompanied, in an inhomogeneous medium, by a change $-\mathbf{s}\,.\,\text{grad}\;\mu = -u_i\,\partial\mu/\partial x_i$ in μ whilst the third term is associated with an assumed change $(\partial\mu/\partial\tau)\,\delta\tau = -(\partial\mu/\partial\tau)\tau\;\text{div}\;\mathbf{s}$ in μ accompanying a change in density $\delta\tau$.

Although the derivations of (47) proceed by considering energy integrals, it may be questioned whether this completely avoids uncertainties associated with the ambiguity in the energy density w. If, for a material in which B is proportional to H, the expression $w = \frac{1}{2}\mu H^2$ (which gives the total energy correctly) were not to give the actual distribution of energy, then the interpretation of the integral of $\frac{1}{2}\delta\mu H^2$ with the contributions to $\delta\mu$ listed above as the change in energy would be suspect, since derivations of W do not include any consideration of a deformation of the medium. In practice, however, it is difficult to see how physically acceptable modifications can be made to w in such a way as to leave W the same whilst leading to a different expression for **g**. Indeed, Stratton has concluded that there appears to be little reason to doubt that the Helmholtz theory is fundamentally sound. Other authors have remained unconvinced but their objections are not discussed here and the Helmholtz theory is the only one that is considered. However, because the matter is to a certain extent controversial, the criticisms of the Helmholtz theory advanced below are confined to those that can be made of any general method of this type.

There is some experimental evidence (Hakim 1962) that (47a) is correct for non-polar dielectric liquids but for a solid material there is clearly an objection in principle to representing the permeability by a scalar, for magnetization is accompanied by strain and this strain may destroy the isotropy exhibited by the material in the unstrained state. The permeability must therefore be represented by a tensor μ_{ij}, so that $B_i = \mu_{ij}H_j$, with a reduction to the scalar $\mu_{ij} = \mu\,\delta_{ij}$ only in the unstrained state. The effect on μ_{ij} of changes in strain—which may, of course, be effected without change in volume—can be accommodated by postulating a linear relationship of the form

$$\delta\mu_{ij} = b_{ijkl}\,\delta E_{kl}, \tag{48}$$

where $b_{ijkl} = \partial\mu_{ij}/\partial E_{kl}$. This case is again considered in detail by Stratton (1941) who shows for a medium that is initially isotropic, although not necessarily homogeneous, that there are only two independent non-zero b_{ijkl}, namely $b_1 = b_{1111}$ and $b_2 = b_{1122}$, and that

$$g_i = \varepsilon_{ijk}J_jB_k - \tfrac{1}{2}H^2\frac{\partial\mu}{\partial x_i} - \tfrac{1}{2}\frac{\partial}{\partial x_j}[(b_1 - b_2)H_iH_j + b_2H^2\delta_{ij}]. \tag{49}$$

A complete account of this theory is given by Pockels (1906): he gives references to the older literature and also deals with the extension to anisotropic media and with the case in which the permeability is field dependent.

As indicated in 3.4(a), the surface stress $\mathbf{\Lambda}$ arises because of the rapid variation in $\mathbf{g}$ at the bounding surface of the body. Using the result $\mathbf{J} = \text{curl } \mathbf{H}$, it is possible to show that $\varepsilon_{ijk}J_jB_k$ is equal to $B_j\,\partial H_i/\partial x_j - B_j\,\partial H_j/\partial x_i$ (Problem 7), and, since div $\mathbf{B} = 0$, (49) may be written in the form of (54a) of 3.4, where

$$\Lambda_i - \Lambda_i^* = a_{ij} = \tfrac{1}{2}[(b_1 - b_2)H_iH_j + (b_2H^2 + I_kH_k)\delta_{ij}], \tag{50}$$

(*d*) *Criticisms of the Helmholtz theory.* Closer examination reveals that there are a number of objections which can be made to the general method that leads to (49) and to its generalisation for the case in which permeability is field dependent. First, it may be observed that the presence of ferromagnetic domains is ignored in regarding the material as a continuum. However, although it is true that a consideration of domains would be essential in considering single crystals, it will be assumed, as in 2.3(f), that in polycrystalline materials the domain structure is sufficiently broken up by the existence of the individual crystalline grains for the Helmholtz method to be appropriate provided that conditions are not investigated on a scale comparable with the size of the grains.† Secondly, it may be queried whether a specification of strain in terms of the displacement gradients E_{kl} is adequate since these are known to be

† Above saturation, where this criticism is inappropriate, (50) predicts that the strain will be field-dependent. However, the dependence observed experimentally is too small—as indicated in 4.3—for useful conclusions to be drawn in relation to equation (50).

satisfactory measures of strain only to first order. A rigorous treatment of this mater involves the use of finite strain theory (in which the displacement gradients are not assumed to be satisfactory measures of strain). This requires the use of two-point tensor fields, which are considered to be outside the scope of the present book, but the problem has been treated satisfactorily (Toupin 1956, 1963, Eringen 1962) and it seems reasonably certain that the Helmholtz theory is not invalidated by using the E_{kl} as measures of strain. The third criticism of the Helmholtz theory is that the parameters b_1 and b_2 are not as significant as they appear to be: this is considered in detail in 4.2(e). Finally, it should be noted that the theory does not predict deformation. Remembering that the body force density **g** can not be obtained either from kinematic observations or from experiments in which part of a material body is separated from the remainder, the absence of any prediction of strain may be seen to be unfortunate, for deformations may be readily measured provided the body is in static equilibrium. Moreover, with the advent of resistance strain gauges of very small dimensions it is now a practical proposition to make local measurements of strain rather than measurements of overall changes in length. However, an immediate comparison of such data with the Helmholtz theory is not possible since this theory offers no guidance as to the values to be ascribed to m_{ij} and E_{ij}^{o}. More recent extensions of the Helmholtz theory have suggested that the stress m_{ij} may be determined by making assumptions about the form of the energy density (Toupin 1956, Eringen 1962, Chu, Haus and Penfield 1966) or, alternatively, about the form of the constitutive law relating **I** to **H** (Penfield and Haus 1966). Again, however, the question of deformation is left open and an immediate comparison with measurements of strain can not be effected.

In principle it is possible to proceed—as in the thermal analogy discussed in 4.2(a)—by enquiring whether a theory predicts the observed deformations of a number of different materials, preferably by relating the deformations to the individual atomic or molecular constitutions of these materials. Unfortunately there is an almost complete absence of measurements of magnetic strain in any other than uniform fields. There is clearly scope here for a systematic investigation of the relation between local deformation and magnetic field conditions but at the present time the data simply do not exist.

There is an abundance of data on the magnetic deformation produced in the absence of conduction currents by uniform fields, but under these conditions $\mathbf{g} = 0$ and the only check on the theory is provided by formulae such as (50) for $\mathbf{\Lambda}$. However, unless b_1 and b_2 can be determined there is no more information content in (50) than in the result (54) of 3.4(c)—which was derived independently of the Helmholtz theory.

(*e*) *The significance of* b_1 *and* b_2. The main attraction of the Helmholtz method is that it apprently relates the force density $\mathbf{g}$ to two parameters, $b_1 = \partial\mu_{11}/\partial E_{11}$ and $b_2 = \partial\mu_{11}/\partial E_{22}$, which can be determined experimentally: the measurement of permeability is, after all, a straightforward matter and no essential difficulty is introduced in making measurements on a specimen in a state of strain. To appreciate that this attraction is largely illusory it is necessary to consider the relevence of the second remark of Stratton quoted in 4.2(c)—that concerning reversibility. In the Helmholtz theory B is assumed to be a single-valued function of H and hysteresis is therefore specifically excluded. How relevant is it then to a real material such as iron which exhibits hysteresis? If the hysteresis is reduced the area of the loop shown in Fig. 4.2 is correspondingly reduced and it is tempting therefore to imagine that the virgin curve a, or some similar curve, represents the magnetization curve of hysteresis-less iron. In this way measurements of the energy of the actual iron could be related to that of ideal iron which exhibits no hysteresis. However, the magnetization curve for ideal iron would, in fact, be quite different from curve a of Fig. 4.2.

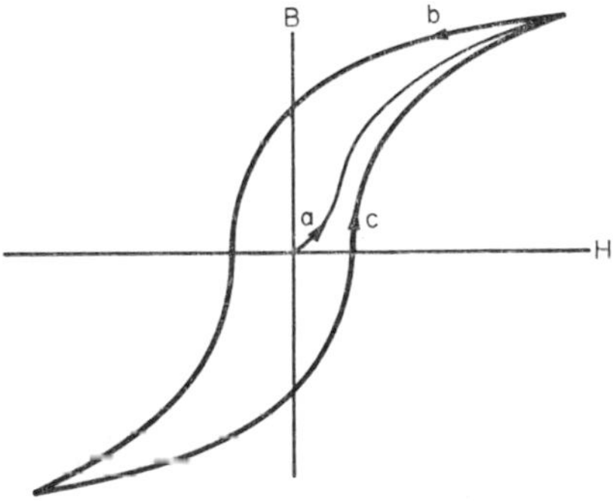

Fig. 4.2

A polycrystalline magnetic material like iron is divided, when demagnetized, into a number of regions, called domains, each of which is magnetized to saturation. The directions of these domain magnetizations are distributed substantially at random because of the varying orientations of the individual crystalline grains. In low fields magnetization proceeds by domain boundary movements, that is the boundary or wall separating two adjacent domains moves so that a favourably orientated domain grows at the expense of its less favourably orientated neighbour. In iron there are two types of wall motions called 180° and 90° boundary movements, corresponding to the movement of walls separating antiparallel domains and walls separating perpendicular domains. The two types of boundaries are depicted diagrammatically in Figs. 4.3(a) and 4.3(b), in which

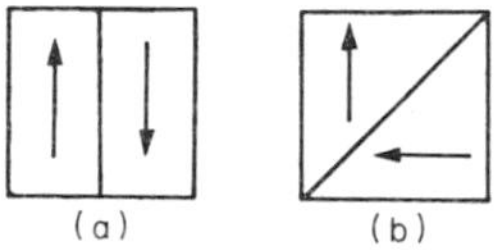

Fig. 4.3

the arrows indicate the direction of domain magnetization.† In higher fields, after the motion of domain boundaries is completed, the magnetization proceeds by the rotation of the magnetization vector within each domain towards the direction of the applied magnetic field.

Now if a single crystal were to have zero hysteresis this would imply that there would be no resistance to 180° boundary movements. Such resistance arises because of the existence of imperfections in the material (Morrish 1965), where the term imperfections is used in a general sense to include imperfections in the form of impurities, of local regions of stress and of holes or inclusions. A lack of hysteresis implies that such imperfections have been removed (by suitable chemical purification and thermal annealing) so that 180° boundary movements proceed reversibly and without resistance. It will be assumed, for the moment, that the elimination of imperfections also

† In low fields the domain magnetizations can only be directed substantially along the easy directions, that is along the cubic crystallographic axes of the individual crystallite within the polycrystalline aggregate.

means that 90° boundary movements proceed without resistance. This assumption—which will be modified at a later stage—means that all domain boundary movements proceed reversibly and without resistance in a single crystal. However, in a polycrystalline material domain wall motion is impeded by the presence of grain boundaries even when imperfections are absent. The assumption of zero hysteresis is therefore equivalent to considering an ideal polycrystalline material consisting of many crystalline grains but with no grain boundaries between them.

Setting aside the conceptual difficulties involved here, the magnetization of the ideal material would proceed after the boundary movements are completed, by the rotation of the magnetization vectors in each domain towards the field direction and against crystalline anisotropy forces. This part of the magnetization curve is calculable (Becker and Döring 1939) and corresponds to the portion *PQ* of the diagrammatic representation *d* of the magnetization curve shown in Fig. 4.4. The initial vertical section *OP* corresponds to the fact that in the ideal material the unimpeded boundary movements proceed in infinitesimal fields.† Clearly, the measurement of areas on curve *a* of Fig. 4.2 to calculate the energy density w will yield values that are not the same as those calculated from the magnetization curve of the ideal material shown as curve *d* in Fig. 4.4. The discrepancy will be particularly pronounced in the initial stages of the magnetization process where B is not a single-valued function of H for the ideal material. The ideal curve conforms to the intuitive requirement that it lies between *b* and *c* of Fig. 4.2 but it can not be identified with the virgin curve *a*.

It is now convenient to return to the question of whether 90° boundary movements can proceed without opposition. In fact, the change of magnetization involved in one domain growing at the expense of its orthogonally orientated neighbour is accompanied by an alteration in the magnetostrictive deformation of the domain. Clearly, if the domains formed a pattern that could be fitted together without localized stresses before the movement of the 90° boundary, this will not be the case afterwards since the shape of the pieces making up the pattern (i.e. the domains) will be different because of

† For a specimen with a finite demagnetizing factor, the field referred to is not the externally applied field, H^o, but the internal field, H.

the alteration in the magnetostrictive deformation. A certain amount of energy would therefore be required to fit the new pattern together and this would be stored in the form of elastic energy. It is for this reason that, in practice, 180° boundary movements—which do not involve any alteration in the magnetostrictive deformation—proceed before 90° boundary movements. This being so, the initial part of the magnetization curve of the ideal material must still be vertical and the nett effect of the change in magnetostriction associated with 90° boundary movements is to modify the curve *d* of Fig. 4.4 in some such way as indicated by the broken curve, *e*. The

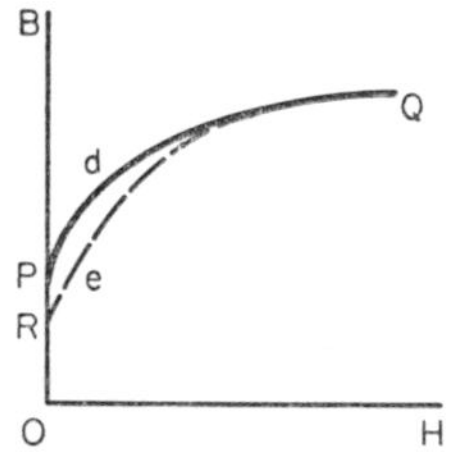

Fig. 4.4

broken curve is still reversible but it cannot be calculated in an exact way as can curve *d*. In this connection it may be noticed that, in practice, there will also be elastically stored energy due to the presence of grain boundaries as well as due to the presence of 90° walls in the actual material. However, this is a comment on the difference between the ideal material and the actual material; it does not affect the initial course of the magnetization curve for the former.

A further difference between the ideal material and the actual material is that there is a possibility of different demagnetized states in the latter. Although the demagnetized state must be one in which the bulk magnetization is zero, the distribution of domain magnetization vectors need not be completely isotropic, as is indicated in Fig. 4.5. Fig. 4.5(a) represents diagrammatically the ideal demagnetized state in which the distribution of domain vectors is isotropic, whilst Fig. 4.5(b) represents a demagnetized state in which there is a preferential alignment of domain vectors. In both states the magnetization is zero but it is found (Lee 1953) that demagnetized states involving preferential domain alignment can be produced in practice, for example, by different methods of demagnetization. It may be noted that in the unstrained ideal material the demagnetized state represented in Fig. 4.5(b) is impossible for a random distribution of crystalline grains because (although all the domain magnetization vectors could be in easy directions) the energy of the arrangement would not be as small as that represented in Fig. 4.5(a). For a real material, however, the situation shown in Fig. 4.5(b) *can*

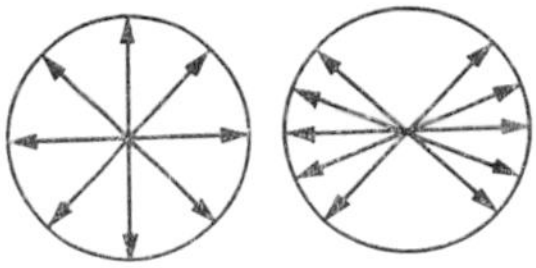

Fig. 4.5

arise because of the resistance to wall motion. Since the motion of the domain boundaries is not completely reversible, it is possible for an individual wall to occupy a position of *local* minimum energy without the energy of the whole arrangement of domains being a minimum. This represents a further discrepancy between the behaviour of the ideal and the actual material.

The ideal material is thus seen to possess a magnetization curve in which appreciable magnetization takes place in infinitesimal fields, so that the relationship between B and H is not single-valued. Indeed, the assumption of zero hysteresis is incompatible with the assumption of a single-valued relationship between B and H: the elimination of hysteresis leads automatically to B being a multi-valued function of H.

The above discussion has emphasised the differences between the magnetization curve for a real ferromagnetic material and for an ideal material in which hysteresis has been eliminated. Unfortunately, it is the behaviour of the ideal material that is of interest in investigating the stresses and strains in a magnetic body. This can be appreciated by considering Fig. 4.6, in which the broken curve e of Fig. 4.4. has been superimposed on to part of the hysteresis loop shown in Fig. 4.2. In the initial magnetization process in which the material is taken up the virgin curve a to the point Q, the amount of energy required is given by the area OQS. On reducing the field to zero, energy of amount TQS is recovered, and this therefore represents stored energy. However, some of the energy stored at Q will have been lost by irreversible processes as the field is reduced. The

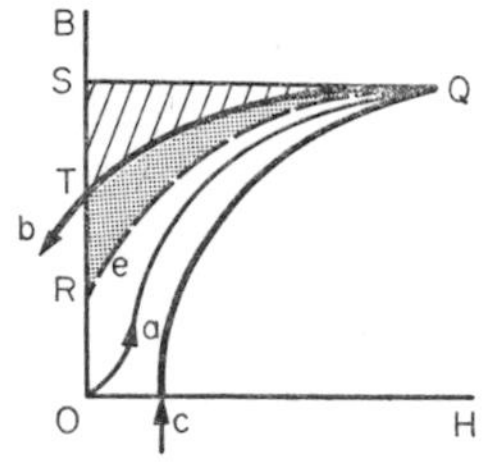

Fig. 4.6

energy stored at Q is therefore not TQS but RQS, where the curve e is, by definition, that appropriate to the ideal material. The concept of stored energy is thus useful only in so far as it can be obtained for the ideal material. Moreover, in studying magneto-mechanical phenomena it is necessary to know the stored energy for the ideal material not only for all values of H but also for different deformations. It is impossible to obtain this information experimentally because the ideal material is not accessible to experimental observation. In particular, it may be noted that the possibility of preferential alignment of domain vectors in the demagnetized state is important in the presence of a deformation of the material. Furthermore, remembering that it is the behaviour of the ideal material that is of interest, it may be seen that an attempt to impose linearity on the relationship between permeability and strain by writing down a formal linear relationship such as (48) connecting $\delta\mu_{ij}$ and δE_{kl} is not in accordance with the conclusions reached above. If the magnetization attains a finite value in infinitesimal fields as shown in Fig. 4.4, the permeability is effectively infinite for this range of B and the relationship given by (48) is therefore clearly inappropriate.

In conclusion, therefore, the apparent attraction of the Helmholtz theory in relating **g** to the parameters b_1 and b_2 is illusory since they do not refer to the actual material of interest but to an ideal material which is not accessible to experimental observation. Furthermore, the demagnetized state—far from forming a natural reference state—is subject to considerable ambiguity and the only completely unambiguous state is the magnetically saturated state. A ferromagnetic material like iron is always magnetized to saturation on a microscopic scale and the saturated single domain should, ideally, be taken as a starting point, the behaviour of the bulk material being obtained by suitable averaging procedures. It may therefore be concluded that the Helmholtz theory does not permit satisfactory predictions to be made of the stresses and strains produced by ponderomotive forces, for it does not permit theory and experiment to be related for a range of different materials. To make any progress in this direction it is necessary to consider the theories of solid-state physics.

4.3 The theories of solid-state physics

Solid-state physics is the branch of physics in which attempts are made to relate the properties of solid materials to their known individual atomic or molecular constitutions. For example, when a nickel rod is magnetized longitudinally to saturation by a uniform field its length decreases by about 0.0034%, whilst for iron the corresponding figure is 0.0007%: it should be possible, in principle, to predict these numbers from the known atomic properties of the two individual elements, and such a task falls within the province of solid-state physics. The theories that are used in this branch of physics are mainly quantum-mechanical in nature and are sufficiently specialised to be completely outside the scope of the present book. Nevertheless it is necessary to refer to the predictions of such theories if they are to be used in considering the stresses and strains produced by ponderomotive forces.

The basis of the theories is a consideration of the intermolecular forces acting between neighbouring or near-neighbouring molecules, and in particular of the dependence of these forces upon intermolecular distances, and hence upon deformation. The conditions assumed correspond to homogeneous macroscopic magnetization, a situation that obtains in practice within a single ferromagnetic domain and also for a single-crystal specimen magnetized to saturation. The applicability of the theories is also restricted to single crystals by the assumption that the molecules are disposed so as to form a regular crystallographic lattice: this assumption facilitates calculation, of course, but it is also made in recognition of the fact that the crystalline state is the natural one for most solids. The corresponding stress in the body regarded as a continuum is not used as an intermediate concept, and the prediction of a uniform strain follows directly from the consideration of a molecule and its near neighbours and from the assumption of homogeneity.

The extent of the agreement of the predicted strain E^o_{ij}, which is uniform, with the strain $E^{\mathscr{I}}_{ij}$ observed experimentally is discussed below, where it is concluded that E^o_{ij} is the dominant contribution to $E^{\mathscr{I}}_{ij}$. As in the thermal situation considered in 4.2(a), a prediction of uniform strain—even if in substantial agreement with experiment—does not dictate whether the strain is spontaneous or produced through the operation of a stress. However, the theories lend no support to the existence of the surface stress needed to maintain the stress corresponding to E^o_{ij} and consequently E^o_{ij} must be classified as a spontaneous strain. Although the theories do not predict the existence of the strain E^*_{ij} arising from the surface stresses $\mathbf{\Lambda}^*$ of 3.4(c), which is generally much smaller than E^o_{ij}, this is because only the dominant, short-range, interparticle forces are considered, so that the effect of the long-range dipole-dipole forces is not included. This necessitates a separate calculation of the form effect (the shape-dependence of strain) and this must be borne in mind when interpreting experimental results.

For a saturated single crystal the theories predict a uniform spontaneous strain which does not depend on the shape of the body. To a first approximation they also predict that the strain will be independent of the applied field used to saturate the crystal. This book is concerned primarily with isotropic (or polycrystalline) materials but there is, in fact, an abundance of magnetostriction data on single crystals and these provide the most direct check on theoretical predictions. In addition, it is not possible to predict the deformation of a polycrystal from single-crystal data unless some simplifying assumptions (Vladimirsky 1943, Lee 1955) are made about the shape of the individual crystalline grains, and therefore about the way in which they interact elastically. For single crystals, the deformation below saturation can not readily be related to that at saturation for a number of reasons (Birss and Hegarty 1966) one of which is that the detailed arrangement of the domain pattern is known only for a few special cases. This difficulty applies with even more force when externally applied stresses are present, so that the theories must be judged, essentially by comparison with magnetostriction measurements made at saturation on freely supported single-crystal specimens, ideally of ellipsoidal shape.

The exact form of the expressions governing the saturation deformation of polycrystals and single crystals is considered in Chapter 5 but it is sufficient here to note that the fractional change in length in the direction of a unit vector $\boldsymbol{\beta}$ for magnetization in the direction of a unit vector $\boldsymbol{\alpha}$ may be written as a sum of angular functions $f_k(\boldsymbol{\alpha}, \boldsymbol{\beta})$ each multiplied by a corresponding coefficient B_k. Crystallographic or isotropic symmetry may be used to impose restrictions on the forms of the f_k and it is found, in practice, that only the functions of the lower orders in the α_i are important. The f_k contain no arbitrary constants and the predictions of theory thus relate to the values of the magnetostriction constants B_k. The theories must therefore be judged on a comparison with the experimental values of the B_k (for small k) and with the prediction of a uniform spontaneous strain at saturation which does not depend on shape and which is, to a first approximation, independent of the applied field.

For the most common ferromagnetic material, iron, the form effect is large because it is proportional to the square of the saturation magnetization. However, measurements on a range of other materials with large B_k and small saturation magnetization have revealed that the magnetostrictive strain is independent of shape for crystals of various forms such as spheroids or thin discs. Nor has any departure from uniformity been noted for these materials, although it must be admitted that the number of direct investigations of local deformation has been extremely small. For practical reasons specimens used in magnetostriction measurements usually have a maximum dimension of the order of one centimetre, and the investigation of the uniformity of strain in such a specimen necessitates the measurement of strains over much smaller distances, with a consequent reduction in the actual changes in length of interest. Such an investigation has been carried out (Gersdorf, Stoelinga and Rathenau 1961) for a spherical single crystal of iron, however, and it was found that the strain was uniform after the contribution due to the surface stress $\boldsymbol{\Lambda}^*$ of 3.4(c) had been subtracted. In large enough fields (and at temperatures not too near the Curie point) ferromagnetic materials exhibit a saturation of magnetization which is accompanied by a saturation of strain. For the three common ferromagnetic metals—iron, cobalt and nickel—the experimental values of the magnetostriction constants B_k (for small k) lie within the range from 3×10^{-5} to 5×10^{-4}. Above saturation there is a slight increase of strain with field, H, known as the forced magnetostriction, and it is customary to represent this as a sum of the same angular functions $f_k(\boldsymbol{\alpha}, \boldsymbol{\beta})$ each multiplied by a corresponding parameter HC_k. However, for the same three metals the experimental values of the forced magnetostriction constants C_k are, at most, only of the order of 10^{-12} m A^{-1}, and this effect is thought to be associated with the slight field dependence of the saturation magnetization.† Experimental data thus confirm the prediction of a uniform spontaneous strain at saturation which is, to a first approximation, independent of the applied field.

As far as the size of the coefficients B_k is concerned, all that has been obtained so far is the prediction of values in a few cases. The theories are, at the present time, in an early stage of development: they have not advanced to a stage where it is to be expected that accurate agreement with experiment will be achieved, and present estimates of magnetostriction constants are correct only as to order of magnitude. Nevertheless, some progress has been made in formulating the type of theory called for in 4.2—one in which the behaviour of different materials is related to their known atomic or molecular properties. Theory indicates that, for a single-crystal specimen of ellipsoidal shape magnetized to saturation by a uniform field, the dominant contribution to the magnetic strain, $E_{ij}^{\mathscr{I}}$, is a spontaneous strain, E_{ij}^{o}, that is uniform, shape-independent and, to a first approximation, field-independent. Experiment indicates that the magnetic strain, $E_{ij}^{\mathscr{I}}$, exhibits precisely these characteristics after the contribution due to $\boldsymbol{\Lambda}^*$ has been subtracted. Above saturation, the stress/strain relationship is linear and $\mathbf{g}^{\dagger} = 0$, so that $E_{ij}^{\mathscr{I}} - E_{ij}^{o}$ may conveniently be expressed as the sum of the strain produced by

† The effect is so small that it is difficult to discriminate between a linear and a quadratic variation. For the range of fields used in such measurements, it is possible, in principle, for strains of the same order of magnitude to be produced by the action of stresses of order μH^2, the quadratic coefficients corresponding to the C_k being of order 10^{-17}m^{2}A^{-2}. Moreover, $\mu \simeq \mu_0$ above saturation, which implies that this conclusion should also hold for non-magnetic materials. However, experiments (Anderholm and Peck 1965) on diamagnetic and paramagnetic crystals yield a quadratic dependence on field with coefficients of the order 10^{-19}m^{2}A^{-2} or less.

the surface stress Λ_i^* on the one hand and the strain produced by both the body force density $k_i = -\partial\alpha_{ij}/\partial x_j$ and the surface stress $(\alpha_{ij} - \alpha'_{ij})n_j$ of 3.4(c) on the other. Hence, if the latter strain is uniform, the corresponding stress is uniform, and not only are the k_i zero but also the $(\alpha_{ij} - \alpha'_{ij})$ are constant over the surface of the ellipsoid.

Because E^o_{ij} is considered to be much larger than $E^{\mathscr{I}}_{ij} - E^o_{ij}$ and because local measurements of strain are few in number, there is stronger evidence for the shape-independence of the strain corresponding to the k_i and $(\alpha_{ij} - \alpha'_{ij})$ than for its uniformity. However, the assumption of uniformity can be reinforced by the following argument. At first sight it might be thought to be obvious from symmetry considerations that **g** (and therefore **k**) must be zero for a saturated ellipsoid in a uniform field. However, this conclusion is really appropriate to an infinite medium magnetized to saturation. For a body of finite size the position of an internal volume element will, in general, be asymmetric due to its varying proximity to the surface. In principle, therefore, the k_i may depend upon the shape of the specimen and, strictly speaking, a shape-dependence of the $(\alpha_{ij} - \alpha'_{ij})$ cannot be ruled out. They may all, in principle, depend also on magnetic conditions, but since these are uniform the k_i and the $(\alpha_{ij} - \alpha'_{ij})$ must be constants for a particular field, even if they depend on shape. Hence, for a particular shape and field, both the $(\alpha_{ij} - \alpha'_{ij})n_j = \bar{k}_i$ and the Λ_i^* will integrate to zero over the symmetrical form of the ellipsoid, so that from (51) of 3.4(c) the volume integral of **k**, and therefore **k** itself, must be zero. Furthermore, for a particular shape, the constancy of the $(\alpha_{ij} - \alpha'_{ij})$ means that this surface stress can only give rise to a uniform strain; consequently, since $\mathbf{k} = 0$, the strain arising from the combination of k_i and $(\alpha_{ij} - \alpha'_{ij})n_j$ must be uniform.

It may therefore be concluded that, in the approximation in which the forced magnetostriction is neglected, the present theoretical and experimental position is in complete conformity with the existence, at saturation, of a magnetic strain tensor $E^{\mathscr{I}}_{ij}$ comprising, first, a dominant spontaneous strain E^o_{ij} that is uniform, field-independent and shape-independent, secondly, a smaller, non-uniform, field-independent, shape-dependent strain, E^*_{ij}, produced by the surface stress Λ_i^* and, thirdly, a uniform, field-independent, shape-independent, strain produced by the stress $(\alpha_{ij} - \alpha'_{ij})n_j$ (with $(\alpha_{ij} - \alpha'_{ij})$

constant over the surface). If all the $(\alpha_{ij} - \alpha'_{ij})$ are zero, then $\bar{\mathbf{k}} = 0$ and $\mathbf{\Lambda} = \mathbf{\Lambda}^*$. It has already been seen that $\mathbf{\Lambda}$ certainly contains $\mathbf{\Lambda}^*$. In addition, it may be noted that constant $(\alpha_{ij} - \alpha'_{ij})$ would, in any event, give rise to a uniform, field-independent, shape-independent strain that could be absorbed into the dominant contribution E^o_{ij}—the value of which is not predicted by theory with any great accuracy. It may therefore be concluded that the $(\alpha_{ij} - \alpha'_{ij})$ may well be zero, for the saturated, single-crystal ellipsoid, and since no other values seem to be called for by theory or experiment it will be assumed in what follows that $(\alpha_{ij} - \alpha'_{ij}) = 0$. $E^{\mathscr{I}}_{ij}$ may therefore be regarded as comprising E^o_{ij}, which may be identified with the spontaneous magnetostriction, and E^*_{ij}, which may be identified with the (non-uniform) form effect. In view of the fact that any contribution to the strain due to non-zero $(\alpha_{ij} - \alpha'_{ij})$ could be absorbed into E^o_{ij}, the conclusion $(\alpha_{ij} - \alpha'_{ij}) = 0$ is likely to be disturbed only with the advent of a theory for $\mathbf{g}$ or $\mathbf{\Lambda}$ that supersedes the result (53b) of 3.4 or by the emergence of predicted values for the B_k which are believed to be accurate but which exhibit residual discrepancies with experiment (possibly the same for different materials). The former possibility does not seem likely and, at present, the prospect of the latter can be faced with equanimity.

4.4 Review of the solvability of the problem

In 4.1 it was seen that the problem of specifying the distribution of ponderomotive forces in material bodies cannot be approached by averaging the microscopic force density $\boldsymbol{\zeta}$, unless more information is available about the form of the microscopic fields $\mathbf{e}$ and $\mathbf{b}$. The alternative microscopic method, which involves a consideration of arrays of point dipoles, does not readily provide values of the body force density $\mathbf{g}$ and is, in any event, open to a number of criticisms concerning its applicability to actual dielectric and magnetic materials.

In considering macroscopic theories, Cauchy's stress hypothesis was retained with the modification that the interparticle interactions can contribute to $\mathbf{g}$ as well as to $\mathbf{m}$ (or m_{ij}). Even if $\mathbf{g}$ is known and the mechanical conditions are completely specified,† it is not

† Such a specification might comprise, for example, a prescription $\mathbf{T}^*$ and a specification of the rate of change of momentum (zero in static equilibrium) of every volume element.

possible to proceed immediately to a determination of the tensor m_{ij}—as indicated in 3.4(c)—because of the effect on the stress compatibility equations of the dependence of the stress/strain relationship on magnetization. To determine **g** it is necessary to know how the total force density $g_i + \partial m_{ij}/\partial x_j$ is partitioned into its two constituent terms. No kinematic observation of the rate of change of momentum of the particles contained in a volume element or, equivalently, of the total ponderomotive force **F** will provide this information. Nor do measurements of strain—which are in any event difficult to make except in static equilibrium—serve directly to determine m_{ij} (and hence **g**), since it is not known how much of the deformation is attributable to stress and how much to a spontaneous strain, E^o_{ij}. Moreover, it was concluded in 4.2(b) that the operational 'definition' of stress could not be used either as a theoretical concept, in predicting stress by considering models, or as a practical procedure, since the force on a separated part includes a contribution from the surface of separation which prevents the discovery of what the force on the part would have been had the separation not been made. The only other type of relevant experimental observation that has not so far been considered is that of fracture. If a material fractures at a given stress then the stress can, in principle, be measured thereby. In reality, however, a material breaks not at a given stress but at a given strain,† that is it fractures when the molecules are at such a distance apart that a further increase results in failure of the material. Thus the breaking strain is physically significant and the breaking load, applied mechanically by way of extrinsic forces, is significant but the breaking stress—which is partly a magnetic stress—is ambiguous.

The macroscopic theory of Helmholtz cannot be compared with measurements in non-uniform fields because of the absence of experimental data. Although open to a number of objections—some of which were discussed in 4.2—the Helmholtz theory is the one reproduced in orthodox textbooks (Jeans 1927, Stratton 1941, Abraham and Becker 1950, Durand 1953). In so far as there is an accepted theory governing the distribution of ponderomotive forces in solid materials, the Helmholtz-Korteweg method qualifies for that title, but it should be noted that it offers no guidance as to the values

† In practice, it is necessary also to consider the presence of dislocations.

to be ascribed to the centrally important parameters b_1 and b_2 in equations (49) and (50). Hence, neither the microscopic nor the macroscopic theories permit satisfactory predictions to be made about the distribution of ponderomotive forces, with the exception of the important prognostication that the surface stress $\mathbf{\Lambda}$ must certainly contain $\mathbf{\Lambda}^*$. The theories discussed in 4.3 predict a spontaneous strain directly and it may therefore be concluded that there is, at present, no way of determining the stresses in a material body produced by ponderomotive forces and, therefore, of partitioning the total force $g_i + \partial m_{ij}/\partial x_j$ into its two constituent terms.

In view of the difficulty in determining g_i or $\partial m_{ij}/\partial x_j$ it may be queried whether the partition has any physical significance at all—may it not represent an attempt to divide an observable force into two parts neither of which is separately observable? Setting aside, for reasons discussed above, the possibility of a determination of m_{ij} by an operational procedure or by observations of fracture, stress itself can be recognised only in its terminal aspect—that is as $m_{ij}n_j$. However, since Λ_i is indeterminate to within a quantity $(\alpha_{ij} - \alpha'_{ij})n_j$, the terminal aspect cannot be used to determine the stress; this leaves only the role of stress as an intermediate or auxiliary concept in the calculation of strain. It is therefore possible, in principle, to eliminate the auxiliary concept of stress entirely and to deal exclusively with strain, which is directly observable. However, this would be analagous to attempting to formulate electromagnetism without any reference to fields, since fields are auxiliary concepts that are not themselves directly observable. This is perfectly possible, in principle, but hardly to be recommended in practice in view of the significant advances in electromagnetism that have ensued from the use of the field concept. It is clear that no error can be incurred by expressing the total force as the sum of two terms g_i and $\partial m_{ij}/\partial x_j$, whereas their elimination has at least two disadvantages. First, it results in a loss of conceptual simplicity—since body forces and stresses are familiar concepts—and, secondly, it necessitates a reformulation of the problem if a meaningful way of partitioning the total force density is subsequently discovered. Whether or not these disadvantages are thought to be significant depends on the degree of pessimism or optimism with which this last possibility is contemplated.

The position taken here is that with improvements in the theories of solid-state physics (and those of continuum mechanics) it may eventually become possible to effect the partition in a physically meaningful way. Clearly, this would imply that the terms g_i and m_{ij} would not occur in combination in *all* the relevant equations; for example, the strain might be expected to depend on m_{ij} but not directly on g_i. In view of the foregoing discussion, the distinction between g_i and $\partial m_{ij}/\partial x_j$ can only be given a meaning in relation to deformation, rather than force.† The distinction classifies the state of *knowledge* about the system: as long as it is not known how to distinguish satisfactorily between long-range and short-range inter-particle forces then there will be an ambiguity in the partition of the total force density. Against this background, it is important to ascertain to what extent predictions of strain can be made without this knowledge—that is without a knowledge of α_{ij}. From what has been said above, attention must at present be confined to bodies that are uniformly magnetized‡ and it is with this case that the following two chapters are concerned. The theories of 4.1 and 4.2 do not, of course, permit the determination of the strain but the theories of solid-state physics predict a uniform spontaneous strain for a single-crystal ellipsoid magnetized to saturation in a uniform field and in the absence of applied stresses. The magnetic strain $E_{ij}^{\mathscr{I}}$ may, as discussed in 4.3, be considered to be the sum of this uniform, field-independent, shape-independent strain, E_{ij}^{o}, and a smaller, non-uniform, field-independent, shape-dependent strain, E_{ij}^{*}. This book is concerned primarily with polycrystalline materials, for which attention must again be confined to ellipsoids magnetized to saturation in uniform fields and in the absence of applied stresses. The assumption that $g_i = 0 = (\alpha_{ij} - \alpha'_{ij})$ can then be taken over to the polycrystalline case, so that the magnetic strain $E_{ij}^{\mathscr{I}}$ is partly due to the surface stress $\mathbf{\Lambda}^*$ and partly to the tendency for each crystalline grain to deform spontaneously. The contribution, E_{ij}^{*}, due to $\mathbf{\Lambda}^*$

† Any force density can—as demonstrated for **k** in 3.4(c)—be written as the divergence of a stress tensor. The distinction is therefore physical not mathematical: the stress is assumed to determine the deformation, or more generally, the thermodynamical state.

‡ For uniform magnetization, the idea that the strain is largely the uniform spontaneous strain E_{ij}^{o} rather than a strain arising from surface stresses is attractive, in conformity with the idea that the large Weiss intramolecular field is likely to be of more importance than the applied (or internal) field and spatial gradients thereof.

can be determined by methods that are discussed in Chapter 6. The other contribution—which may again be denoted by E^o_{ij}—cannot be related to the E^o_{ij} appropriate to a single crystal unless some simplifying assumptions are made about the shapes of the individual crystalline grains and about the way in which they interact elastically. However, if the grains are small and orientated at random, the strain E^o_{ij} as measured over distances large compared with the grain size will again be uniform and subject to restrictions imposed by (isotropic) symmetry. The prediction of E^o_{ij} and E^*_{ij} below saturation will not be attempted in what follows because of the difficulty of specifying the pattern of domains throughout the magnetization process (and, incidentally, the resulting form of the magnetization curve).†

In Chapter 5 symmetry restrictions are used to deduce the form of E^o_{ij} for dielectric and for magnetic bodies: the determination of E^*_{ij} is considered in Chapter 6. Both chapters are entirely mathematical in character and the physical discussion of the subject ends at this stage. It turns out that the determination of the E^*_{ij} is a more substantial problem than the determination of the E^o_{ij}.

PROBLEMS 4

1. Show that, in appropriate units, the gravitational potential at an interior point at a distance d from the centre of a sphere of unit density, radius a and volume V is given by

$$\Xi = \iiint_V \frac{1}{r}\, dV = 2\pi(a^2 - \tfrac{1}{3}d^2).$$

[Note that in the integration over angular coordinates different limits must be used for greater and smaller distances than d from the centre.]

2. Show that, for constant μ, the potentials Ω and Ω' given by (7) of 4.2 satisfy the following conditions:
   (i) $\nabla^2\Omega = 0, \nabla^2\Omega' = 0$ (or, equivalently, div $\mathbf{B} = 0$, curl $\mathbf{H} = 0$ everywhere),

† Considerable progress has been made in doing this (Néel 1944, Lawton and Stewart 1948, Birss and Hegarty 1966, Birss, Hegarty and Wallis 1967) but, in general, the field-dependence of the magnetostriction agrees less well with theory than does that of the bulk magnetization.

(ii) $\Omega = \Omega'$, $\mu \partial\Omega/\partial r = \mu_o \partial\Omega'/\partial r$ at all points on the surface of the sphere (or, equivalently, that the tangential components of **H** and the normal components of **B** are continuous),

(iii) $-\text{grad}\ \Omega'$ tends to $\mathbf{H}^o$ as r tends to infinity.

Also show that $\mathbf{H} = -\text{grad}\ \Omega$ and $\mathbf{I} = (\mu - \mu_o)\mathbf{H}$ are uniform and are directed along the x_3-axis with respective magnitudes

$$H = \frac{3\mu_o H^o}{\mu + 2\mu_o}, \qquad I = \frac{3\mu_o(\mu - \mu_o)H^o}{\mu + 2\mu_o}.$$

[Coulson (1953) p. 159.]

3. By direct evaluation show that

$$\int_{u_1}^{0} \left[1 - \frac{\operatorname{sech}^2 u}{1 - k^2}\right] du = \int_{0}^{k} \frac{2z^2\, dz}{(1 - z^2)^2}$$

and then find a relationship $z = f(s)$ that will permit (25) to be written in the form corresponding to (12).

4. Use the substitutions (24) of 4.2 to show that the integral

$$D_{33} = \frac{a_1^2}{2\mu_o a_3^2} \int_{0}^{\pi} \frac{\sin\eta \cos^2\eta\, d\eta}{(a_1^2 \sin^2\eta + a_3^2 \cos^2\eta)^{3/2}}$$

may be put into the form

$$D_{33} = \frac{a_1^2}{\mu_o a_3^2 k^3} \int_{u_1}^{0} \tanh^2 u\, du,$$

and hence verify equation (30).

5. Use the fact that

$$\Xi = \frac{\pi}{m^2 - 1}\left[\frac{m}{\sqrt{m^2 - 1}}(2a^2 + x_1^2 + x_2^2 - 2x_3^2)\cosh^{-1} m \right.$$
$$\left. + 2x_3^2 - m^2(x_1^2 + x_2^2)\right]$$

for a prolate spheroid and that

$$\Xi = \frac{\pi}{1-m^2}\left[\frac{m}{\sqrt{1-m^2}}(2a^2 - x_1^2 - x_2^2 + 2x_3^2)\cos^{-1}m \right.$$
$$\left. - 2x_3^2 + m^2(x_1^2 + x_2^2)\right]$$

for an oblate spheroid to establish equations (29) to (33) of 4.2.

6. Consider the force acting on an element of surface current $\mathbf{K}^* dS$ and, by using the boundary condition relating $\mathbf{B}'$, $\mathbf{B}$ and $\mathbf{K}^*$, show that it may be written in the form

$$\tfrac{1}{2}\mathbf{K}^* \times (\mathbf{B}' + \mathbf{B})\,dS = \frac{1}{\mu_o}\{(\mathbf{I}\times\mathbf{n})\times\mathbf{B} + \tfrac{1}{2}[(\mathbf{I}.\mathbf{n})^2 - I^2]\mathbf{n}\}\,dS\,.$$

Hence show that the stress, $\boldsymbol{X}$, appropriate to the case when $\mathbf{n}$ is parallel to the x_1-axis has the components

$$X_1 = \frac{1}{\mu_o}[I_2B_2 + I_3B_3 - \tfrac{1}{2}(I_2^2 + I_3^2)]\,,$$

$$X_2 = -\frac{1}{\mu_o}I_2B_1\,,$$

$$X_3 = -\frac{1}{\mu_o}I_3B_1\,.$$

7. Prove the identity

$$\varepsilon_{ijs}\varepsilon_{kls} = \delta_{ij}\,\delta_{jl} - \delta_{il}\,\delta_{jk}$$

[Jeffreys (1961) p. 14].

CHAPTER 5

The Prediction of E^o_{ij}

5.1 E^o_{ij} for magnetic and dielectric materials

As indicated in 4.4, symmetry restrictions can be used to deduce the form of E^o_{ij} for dielectric and magnetic bodies. For single crystals this is achieved by using Neumann's principle, which states that any type of geometrical symmetry exhibited by the crystal is possessed by every physical property of the crystal. The (point-group) symmetry of a crystal is described by listing the symmetry operations which, when applied individually to the crystal, leave it in an orientation that is indistinguishable from the original one. For example, for a hexagonal close-packed crystal a symmetry operation is a two-fold rotation about the hexagonal or x_3-axis, to which there corresponds a symmetry matrix

$$\sigma_{ij} = \begin{bmatrix} -1 & 0 & 0 \\ 0 & -1 & 0 \\ 0 & 0 & 1 \end{bmatrix} \tag{1}$$

relating new and old coordinates x'_i and x_i by the equation $x'_i = \sigma_{ij}x_j$, or $x'_1 = -x_1$, $x'_2 = -x_2$, $x'_3 = x_3$. To indicate how the existence of this symmetry matrix can be used to simplify the form of E^o_{ij}, it is necessary to consider some particular term in an expansion for E^o_{ij}, for example the term $b_{ijlm}\alpha_l\alpha_m$. Because of the isotropy of free space, the fourth rank tensor b_{ijlm} is unaltered by a simultaneous two-fold rotation of both the coordinates and the crystal about the x_3-axis, so that the substitution

$$b'_{ijlm} = b_{ijlm} \tag{2a}$$

may be made in the tensor transformation equation

$$b'_{ijlm} = \sigma_{ip}\sigma_{jq}\sigma_{lr}\sigma_{ms}b_{pqrs}\,. \tag{2b}$$

However, the product $\sigma_{ip}\sigma_{jq}\sigma_{lr}\sigma_{ms}$ is -1 when the subscript 3 appears (as p, q, r or s) an odd number of times and, since this implies that $b_{ijlm} = -b_{ijlm}$, all the coefficients b_{ijlm} in which the subscript 3 appears an odd number of times must be identically zero.

These restrictions may be augmented by those corresponding to the presence of other symmetry operations—which are many in number. Fortunately, however, it is possible to eliminate from consideration any operation the application of which is equivalent to the sequential application of two or more operations that have already been considered. In this way it is possible to work with a small number of generating matrices from which all the other symmetry matrices can be obtained by matrix multiplication. For example, all the symmetry matrices for the hexagonal close-packed crystal are generated by four matrices corresponding to inversion through the origin, to a two-fold rotation about the x_2-axis and to three-fold and two-fold rotations about the x_3-axis—the last mentioned being given by (1). If these matrices are substituted in turn into equations (2) it is found (Problem 1) that there are only ten non-zero coefficients b_{ijlm}, namely $b_{1111} = b_{2222} = b_{1122} + b_{1212} + b_{1221}$, $b_{1122} = b_{2211}$, $b_{1212} = b_{2121}$, $b_{1221} = b_{2112}$, b_{3333}, $b_{2323} = b_{1313}$, $b_{2332} = b_{1331}$, $b_{3223} = b_{3113}$, $b_{3232} = b_{3131}$, $b_{1133} = b_{2233}$ and $b_{3311} = b_{3322}$. However, in addition to the symmetry imposed by the crystal structure, the tensor b_{ijlm} exhibits what is called intrinsic symmetry, that is the physical nature of the property it describes causes some of its components to be equal or linearly related. Thus, the last pair of indices in b_{ijlm} is interchangeable because α_l and α_m are interchangeable, whilst the first pair is interchangeable since the tensor E^o_{ij} is symmetric. The number of independent coefficients is thus reduced from ten to six, namely b_{1122}, b_{1133}, b_{3311}, b_{3333}, b_{2332} and b_{1212}, so that, if $b_{ijlm}\alpha_l\alpha_m$ is the only contributions to E^o_{ij},

$$
\begin{aligned}
E^o_{11} &= b_{1122}\alpha_2^2 + b_{1133}\alpha_3^2, \\
E^o_{22} &= b_{1122}\alpha_1^2 + b_{1133}\alpha_3^2, \\
E^o_{33} &= b_{3311}(\alpha_1^2 + \alpha_2^2) + b_{3333}\alpha_3^2, \\
E^o_{23} &= 2b_{2323}\alpha_2\alpha_3 = E^o_{32}, \\
E^o_{31} &= 2b_{2323}\alpha_1\alpha_3 = E^o_{13}, \\
E^o_{12} &= 2b_{1212}\alpha_1\alpha_2 = E^o_{21}.
\end{aligned}
\tag{3}
$$

A similar procedure may be adopted for other types of crystals but in practice it is possible to ascertain the form of b_{ijlm} immediately for any type of crystal from tables that are already in existence (e.g. Birss 1964).

For a magnetic body experimental measurements yield values for the fractional change in length, $\lambda = dl/l$, corresponding to E^o_{ij}, in the direction of a unit vector $\boldsymbol{\beta}$ when the crystal is magnetized to saturation in the direction $\boldsymbol{\alpha}$. It may readily be shown (Problem 2) that

$$\lambda = E^o_{ij}\beta_i\beta_j \tag{4}$$

and (Problem 3) that, on substituting the E^o_{ij} given by (3), λ may be written in the form

$$\lambda = B_o + B_1\beta_3^2 + (B_2 + B_3\beta_3^2)(1 - \alpha_3^2) \\ + [B_4\alpha_3\beta_3 + B_5(\alpha_1\beta_1 + \alpha_2\beta_2)](\alpha_1\beta_1 + \alpha_2\beta_2). \tag{5}$$

The B_k may be identified with the saturation magnetostriction constants, occurring in the expression $\lambda = B_k.f_k(\boldsymbol{\alpha}, \boldsymbol{\beta})$, introduced in 4.3. In the electrical case equation (5) would hold for a saturated ferroelectric or, below saturation, for a dielectric exhibiting distortional polarization. However, the choice of a fourth-rank tensor, b_{ijlm}, as a particular example obscures the fact that there is an important difference between the electrical and magnetic cases. The expression $b_{ijlm}\alpha_l\alpha_m$ is one term of an expansion which may, in general, be written in the form

$$E^o_{ij} = b_{ij} + b_{ijl}\alpha_l + b_{ijlm}\alpha_l\alpha_m + b_{ijlmn}\alpha_l\alpha_m\alpha_n + \dots . \tag{6}$$

In ascertaining the form of the tensors b_{ij}, b_{ijl}, b_{ijlm}, b_{ijlmn}, . . . from the tables referred to above, it is necessary to know whether these tensors are polar or axial, that is whether they remain invariant or change sign under spatial inversion. In the electrical case all the b_{ij}, b_{ijl}, b_{ijlm}, . . . are polar because E^o_{ij} and α_i are polar, and they therefore all transform according to equations similar to (2). These equations are satisfied identically for $\sigma_{ij} = -\delta_{ij}$ if $b_{ijl...}$ is of even rank but lead to the result $b_{ijl...} = -b_{ijl...}$, that is $b_{ijl...} = 0$, if $b_{ijl...}$ is of odd rank. Hence for centrosymmetrical crystals, for which $\sigma_{ij} = -\delta_{ij}$ is a symmetry matrix, all $b_{ijl...}$ of odd rank vanish identically in the electrical case, so that (6) contains only

$b_{ijl...}$ of even rank. In the magnetic case α_i is axial, so that odd-rank $b_{ijl...}$ are axial and even-rank $b_{ijl...}$ are (as in the electrical case) polar. Moreover, the axial tensors are not now zero for $\sigma_{ij} = -\delta_{ij}$, because the transformation equations corresponding to (2) contain an extra minus sign when the tensors are axial. However, it can be shown (Birss 1964) that the restriction to a consideration of saturation and above means that ferromagnetic crystals are effectively invariant under time reversal. It is therefore possible to prove, since $\boldsymbol{\alpha}$ changes sign under time reversal, that the tensors $b_{ijl...}$ of odd rank vanish identically in the magnetic case, whether the crystal is centrosymmetrical or not. Consequently, if (6) represents saturation magnetostriction, the odd-rank $b_{ijl...}$ must be omitted.† They must also be omitted in the electrical case for centrosymmetrical crystals and the resulting equation describes electrostriction: for non-centrosymmetrical crystals the terms involving odd-rank $b_{ijl...}$ are said to describe the inverse piezoelectric effect. Of course, equation (6) is not the only possible expansion for E^o_{ij}: when the dependence of E^o_{ij} on temperature is under consideration a more convenient form of expansion is in terms of surface spherical harmonics $Y_n(\theta, \phi)$ thus:

$$E^o_{ij} = \sum_{n=0}^{\infty} Y_n(\theta,\phi) = \sum_{n=0}^{\infty} [D^{n,o}_{ij} P_n(\cos\theta) + \sum_{m=1}^{n} (D^{n,m}_{ij} \cos m\phi - D^{n,-m}_{ij} \sin m\phi) P^m_n(\cos\theta)], \qquad (7)$$

where the P_n and P^m_n are the usual Legendre functions (MacRobert 1927). However, it is still true that odd (in n) terms are absent both when (7) represents saturation magnetostriction and when it represents the electrical case for centrosymmetrical crystals.

A polycrystalline material is, ideally, an aggregate of a large number of individual crystallites orientated at random. It should therefore be possible, in principle, to relate the polycrystalline E^o_{ij} to the E^o_{ij} appropriate to a single-crystal specimen of the same material. As indicated in 4.4, this is not possible in practice unless some simplifying assumptions are made about the shapes of the individual crystalline grains. If equation (6) is averaged directly

† This conclusion must be modified for certain antiferromagnetic materials (Birss and Anderson 1963).

over a random distribution of crystallite orientations, the odd-rank $b_{ijl\ldots}$ do not contribute to the resultant E^o_{ij}. For cubic and hexagonal materials, the result of retaining even-rank tensors $b_{ijl\ldots}$ up to the sixth rank is to yield (Birss 1960)

$$\lambda = E^o_{ij}\beta_i\beta_j = \xi + \eta \cos^2 \theta , \tag{8}$$

where θ is the angle between the magnetization and the direction of measurement and where ξ and η are linear combinations of the $b_{ijl\ldots}$. The absence of a term in $\cos^4 \theta$ is not surprising for, although terms of fourth order in the α_i have been retained, λ is of second order in the β_i at most and can only depend on $\theta = \boldsymbol{\alpha} . \boldsymbol{\beta}$.

It is possible to derive E^o_{ij} for an isotropic medium by proceeding in the same manner as for single crystals. This may be done by requiring that the $b_{ijl\ldots}$ be isotropic tensors, that is they must be such that their components retain the same values *however* the coordinate axes are rotated. It is well known (Jeffreys 1961) that the only isotropic tensors of ranks two, three and four are respectively

$$\begin{aligned} b_{ij} &= A_1 \delta_{ij} , \\ b_{ijl} &= A_2 \varepsilon_{ijl} , \\ b_{ijlm} &= A_3 \delta_{ij} \delta_{lm} + A_4 \delta_{il} \delta_{jm} + A_5 \delta_{im} \delta_{jl} , \end{aligned} \tag{9}$$

where A_1 to A_5 are arbitrary constants. Inserting (9) into (6) yields

$$E^o_{ij} = A_1 \delta_{ij} + A_2 \varepsilon_{ijl} + A_3 \delta_{ij} + (A_4 + A_5)\alpha_i\alpha_j , \tag{10}$$

since $\alpha_k\alpha_k = 1$. Hence, using (4),

$$\lambda = (A_1 + A_3) + (A_4 + A_5)\alpha_i\beta_i\alpha_j\beta_j , \tag{11}$$

since $\beta_k\beta_k = 1$ and $\varepsilon_{ijl}\beta_i\beta_j\alpha_l = \boldsymbol{\beta} . \boldsymbol{\beta} \times \boldsymbol{\alpha} = 0$. Equation (11) is, of course, identical with (8). The form of isotropic tensors of ranks greater than the fourth can be ascertained when required (Pastori 1930, Caldonazzo 1932) but it is sufficient here to note that the $b_{ijl\ldots}$ of even rank can be written as linear combinations of terms

$$b^e_{ijl\ldots n} = \delta_{qr} \delta_{st} \delta_{uv} \ldots \delta_{yz} , \tag{12a}$$

where $(q, r, s, \ldots y, z)$ is a permutation of $(i, j, l, \ldots n)$, and that the $b_{ijl\ldots}$ of odd rank can be written as linear combinations of terms

$$b^o_{ijl\ldots n} = \varepsilon_{pqr} \delta_{st} \delta_{uv} \ldots \delta_{yz} , \tag{12b}$$

where $(p, q, r, s, \ldots y, z)$ is a permutation of $(i, j, l, \ldots n)$. If i and j are associated with the same δ in $b^e_{ijl\ldots n}$, then, from (6), the contribution of $b^e_{ijl\ldots n}$ to E^o_{ij} is δ_{ij}, whilst if i and j are associated with different δ's the contribution is $\alpha_i\alpha_j$. Unless i and j are both associated with ε in $b^o_{ijl\ldots n}$, the contribution of $b^o_{ijl\ldots n}$ to E^o_{ij} is zero because it contains as a factor either $\boldsymbol{\alpha} \cdot \boldsymbol{\alpha} \times \boldsymbol{\alpha}$ or one component of $\boldsymbol{\alpha} \times \boldsymbol{\alpha}$. The only non-zero contributions are therefore linear combinations of $\varepsilon_{pqr}\alpha_s$, where (p, q, r) is a permutation of (i, j, s). However, these combinations are either zero or are antisymmetric in the indices i and j, which is inconsistent with E^o_{ij} being a symmetrical tensor. Such terms are therefore absent and this constitutes the formal reason why an isotropic medium can not exhibit the inverse (or direct) piezoelectric effect. It may therefore be concluded that the inclusion of isotropic tensors of higher ranks involves little essential modification to equations (10) and that E^o_{ij} may be written in the form

$$E^o_{ij} = \xi\,\delta_{ij} + \eta\alpha_i\alpha_j, \tag{13}$$

so that

$$\lambda = E^o_{ij}\beta_i\beta_j = \xi + \eta\alpha_i\beta_i\alpha_j\beta_j, \tag{14}$$

in agreement with equation (8).

PROBLEMS 5

1. Determine the four symmetry matrices corresponding to inversion through the origin, to a two-fold rotation about the x_2-axis and to two-fold and three-fold rotations about the x_3-axis. Establish by using equation (2) that the first leads to no simplification in the form of the (polar) tensor b_{ijlm}, that the second and third lead to 60 components being identically zero and that the fourth leads to the reduction of the remaining 21 to the ten non-zero coefficients $b_{1111} = b_{2222} = b_{1122} + b_{1212} + b_{1221}$, $B_{1122} = b_{2211}$, $b_{1212} = b_{2121}$, $b_{1221} = b_{2112}$, b_{3333}, $b_{2323} = b_{1313}$, $b_{2332} = b_{1331}$, $b_{3223} = b_{3113}$, $b_{3232} = b_{3131}$, $b_{1133} = b_{2233}$ and $b_{3311} = b_{3322}$ [Birss (1964) p. 50].

2. Show that, for small strains, the fractional change in length in a direction $\boldsymbol{\beta}$ of a small element of length originally parallel to

the unit vector $\boldsymbol{\beta}$ is given by $E_{ij}\beta_i\beta_j$, where E_{ij} is the symmetrical strain tensor [Birss (1959) p. 255].

3. Verify that the substitution of (3) into (4) yields an expression that can be written in the form (5). [Note that $\alpha_k\alpha_k = 1 = \beta_k\beta_k$.]

4. Relate $Y_2(\theta, \phi)$ of (7) to the b_{ij} and b_{ijlm} of (6) [Birss (1964) p. 165].

CHAPTER 6

The Prediction of E_{ij}^{*}

6.1 Introduction

As indicated in 4.4, the prediction of the non-uniform strain, E_{ij}^{*}, produced by the surface stress $\mathbf{\Lambda}^{*}$ constitutes a more substantial problem† than that of predicting the form of E_{ij}^{o}. In the magnetic case

$$\mathbf{\Lambda}^{*} = \frac{1}{2\mu_o}(\mathbf{I}\,.\,\mathbf{n})^2\mathbf{n}, \tag{1}$$

and the resulting deformation is known as the (non-uniform) form effect. Only conditions at saturation are considered here and the size of the saturation form effect is clearly proportional to the square of the saturation magnetization, I_s: for iron $I_s \simeq 2.2$ Weber m^{-2} so that $I_s^2/2\mu_o \simeq 1.9 \times 10^6 N$ m^{-2}. In what follows the calculation of E_{ij}^{*} will be presented, for convenience, in magnetic terms and indeed published discussions of the form effect invariably refer to the magnetic case. Although the corresponding electrical form effect is not usually considered it should not, in fact, be neglected for ferroelectrics. For example, barium titanate has a saturation polarization given by $P_s \simeq 0.26$ Coulomb m^{-2} which corresponds to $P_s^2/2\varepsilon_o \simeq 3.8 \times 10^9 N$ m^{-2}.

The first case of a successful prediction of E_{ij}^{*} was provided by the work of Gersdorf (1960) who considered a sphere of radius R saturated parallel to the x_3-axis, so that

$$\Lambda_i^{*} = \frac{I_s^2}{2\mu_o}\frac{x_3^2}{R^2}n_i. \tag{2}$$

Body forces are absent and, from symmetry, $\mathbf{\Lambda}^{*}$ integrates to zero over the surface of the sphere, which can therefore remain in equilibrium with no additional surface stresses $\mathbf{T}^{*}$. Above saturation, the

† It may be noted that, since E_{ij}^{*} is non-uniform, it can not be calculated by the methods of Powell (1931) and Becker (1934), although these methods can be used if only the volume averages of the strains are required (Gersdorf 1960).

stress/strain relationship is linear and the elastic constants have their non-magnetic values as indicated in 3.4(b), so that, from (34) of 3.3, $m_{ij} = m'_{ij}$ and E_{ij} are related by

$$m_{ij} = 2GE_{ij} + \frac{2G\nu}{1-2\nu}\varepsilon\,\delta_{ij}, \tag{3a}$$

$$E_{ij} = \frac{1}{2G}m_{ij} - \frac{\nu}{Y}\Theta\,\delta_{ij}, \tag{3b}$$

where $G = Y/2(1+\nu)$ is the rigidity (or shear) modulus. The stress tensor, m_{ij}, corresponding to $\mathbf{\Lambda}^*$ must therefore satisfy not only (43) and (44) of 3.4(a) but also a compatibility equation of the same type as (39) of 3.3. Hence m_{ij} must satisfy the equations

$$\frac{\partial m_{ij}}{\partial x_j} = 0 \tag{4}$$

and

$$\nabla^2 m_{ij} + \frac{1}{1+\nu}\frac{\partial^2 M}{\partial x_i \partial x_j} = 0, \tag{5}$$

where $M = m_{kk}$, together with the boundary conditions

$$m_{ij}n_j = \frac{I_s^2}{2\mu_o}\frac{x_3^2}{R^2}n_i. \tag{6}$$

For this simple case the stress components do not involve higher powers of the coordinates than the second and it may be readily shown (Gersdorf 1960) that the m_{ij} are given by

$$\begin{aligned} m_{11} &= \frac{I_s^2}{2\mu_o}\left\{\frac{x_3^2}{R^2} + \frac{\nu}{5\nu+7}\left[1 - \frac{x_1^2}{R^2} - 5\frac{x_2^2}{R^2} + \frac{x_3^2}{R^2}\right]\right\}, \\ m_{22} &= \frac{I_s^2}{2\mu_o}\left\{\frac{x_3^2}{R^2} + \frac{\nu}{5\nu+7}\left[1 - 5\frac{x_1^2}{R^2} - \frac{x_2^2}{R^2} + \frac{x_3^2}{R^2}\right]\right\}, \\ m_{33} &= \frac{I_s^2}{2\mu_o}\left\{1 - \frac{x_1^2}{R^2} - \frac{x_2^2}{R^2} + \frac{2\nu}{5\nu+7}\left[-1 + 2\frac{x_1^2}{R^2} + 2\frac{x_2^2}{R^2} + \frac{x_3^2}{R^2}\right]\right\}, \end{aligned} \tag{7}$$

$$m_{12} = m_{21} = \frac{I_s^2}{2\mu_o}\left[\frac{4\nu}{5\nu+7}\frac{x_1x_2}{R^2}\right],$$

$$m_{23} = m_{32} = \frac{I_s^2}{2\mu_o}\left[-\frac{2\nu}{5\nu+7}\frac{x_2x_3}{R^2}\right], \qquad (7)$$

$$m_{31} = m_{13} = \frac{I_s^2}{2\mu_o}\left[-\frac{2\nu}{5\nu+7}\frac{x_3x_1}{R^2}\right].$$

It should be noted that the stress already depends on the elastic properties of the material because of the occurrence of Poisson's ratio, ν, in (7). The corresponding strains may be obtained immediately from (3b) and the subsequent integration of (22) of 3.2 to obtain the displacements, u_i, gives

$$u_1 = -\frac{I_s^2(2\nu+3)\nu}{\mu_o Y(5\nu+7)}x_1 + \frac{I_s^2(1+\nu)\nu}{\mu_o Y(5\nu+7)R^2}x_1(x_1^2+x_2^2) + \frac{I_s^2(1+\nu)(7-8\nu)}{2\mu_o Y(5\nu+7)R^2}x_1x_3^2,$$

$$u_2 = -\frac{I_s^2(2\nu+3)\nu}{\mu_o Y(5\nu+7)}x_2 + \frac{I_s^2(1+\nu)\nu}{\mu_o Y(5\nu+7)R^2}x_2(x_1^2+x_2^2) + \frac{I_s^2(1+\nu)(7-8\nu)}{2\mu_o Y(5\nu+7)R^2}x_2x_3^2, \qquad (8)$$

$$u_3 = \frac{I_s^2(7+3\nu-2\nu^2)}{2\mu_o Y(5\nu+7)}x_3 - \frac{I_s^2(1+\nu)(7-6\nu)}{2\mu_o Y(5\nu+7)R^2}(x_1^2+x_2^2)x_3 - \frac{2I_s^2(1+\nu)\nu}{\mu_o Y(5\nu+7)R^2}x_3^3.$$

In conformity with the symmetry of the problem, the displacement has no component perpendicular to planes containing the x_3-axis.

6.2 An analytical method

In seeking solutions for the u_i for more general shapes than that of a sphere, it is desirable to adopt some systematic method of procedure, such as is provided by the use (described below) of Papkovitch-Neuber stress functions. It is also advantageous to formulate the problem in a system of coordinates that has the same symmetry as the geometry of the sample. However, a change of coordinates may affect the formulation of the elastic properties of the medium and it is necessary to take this into consideration. In the rectangular Cartesian co-ordinates, x_i, the stress/strain relationship for an isotropic medium is provided by (3). Moreover, this equation is true at every point and remains true when the coordinates are changed to orthogonal curvilinear coordinates, X_i, provided the same definitions are used for m_{ij} and E_{ij}. The components, m_{ij}, of the stress tensor in curvilinear coordinates are defined in exactly the same way as they were in 3.1 for Cartesian coordinates, m_{ij} being the ith component of the stress acting across an elementary area orientated perpendicular to the jth coordinate line. However, when the geometrical interpretation of the strain components, E_{ij}, discussed in 3.2 is retained, it is no longer true that these are related to the components of the displacement, U_i, by $E_{ij} = \frac{1}{2}(\partial U_i/\partial X_j + \partial U_j/\partial X_i)$, since an increment dX_i in X_i does not always, in curvilinear coordinates, correspond to a displacement in space of the same magnitude.

If only one of the X_i is varied to give an infinitesimal displacement or line element dl_i in space, then $dl_i = h_i\, dX_i$ and, for a general displacement,†

$$dl^2 = h_1^2\, dX_1^2 + h_2^2\, dX_2^2 + h_3^2\, dX_3^2. \tag{9}$$

With this notation it can be shown by a detailed geometrical analysis (Sokolnikoff 1956) that the strain components E_{ij} and the displacements U_i are connected by the relations

$$E_{ij} = \frac{1}{2h_i h_j}\left[h_i^2 \frac{\partial}{\partial X_j}\left(\frac{U_i}{h_i}\right) + h_2^2 \frac{\partial}{\partial X_i}\left(\frac{U_j}{h_j}\right)\right] + \frac{\delta_{ij}}{2h_i^2}\sum_{k=1}^{3}\frac{\partial h_i^2}{\partial X_k}\left(\frac{U_k}{h_k}\right). \tag{10}$$

(In this equation and in subsequent ones in this chapter, the summation convention is assumed not to operate for any equation in

† The quantities h_i are related to the metric coefficients

$$g_{ij} = (\partial x_k/\partial X_i)(\partial x_k/\partial X_j) \text{ by}$$

$$h_1 = \sqrt{g_{11}}, \qquad h_2 = \sqrt{g_{22}}, \qquad h_3 = \sqrt{g_{33}},$$

the other components being zero because the curvilinear coordinates are orthogonal.

which a summation is indicated explicitly.) For spherical polar coordinates (r, θ, ϕ),

$$x_1 = r\sin\theta\cos\phi, \qquad X_1 = r = \sqrt{x_1^2 + x_2^2 + x_3^2},$$

$$x_2 = r\sin\theta\sin\phi, \qquad X_2 = \theta = \tan^{-1}\left[\frac{\sqrt{x_1^2 + x_2^2}}{x_3}\right], \tag{11}$$

$$x_3 = r\cos\theta, \qquad X_3 = \phi = \tan^{-1}\left[\frac{x_2}{x_1}\right],$$

and

$$h_1 = 1, \qquad h_2 = r, \qquad h_3 = r\sin\theta, \tag{12}$$

so that equations (10) may be particularized to the forms

$$E_{rr} = \frac{\partial U_r}{\partial r},$$

$$E_{\theta\theta} = \frac{1}{r}\frac{\partial U_\theta}{\partial \theta} + \frac{U_r}{r},$$

$$E_{\phi\phi} = \frac{1}{r\sin\theta}\frac{\partial U_\phi}{\partial \phi} + \frac{U_r}{r} + U_\theta\frac{\cot\theta}{r},$$

$$E_{r\phi} = \tfrac{1}{2}\left[\frac{1}{r\sin\theta}\frac{\partial U_r}{\partial \phi} - \frac{U_\phi}{r} + \frac{\partial U_\phi}{\partial r}\right], \tag{13}$$

$$E_{r\theta} = \tfrac{1}{2}\left[\frac{1}{r}\frac{\partial U_r}{\partial \theta} - \frac{U_\theta}{r} + \frac{\partial U_\theta}{\partial r}\right],$$

$$E_{\phi\theta} = \tfrac{1}{2}\left[\frac{1}{r}\frac{\partial U_\phi}{\partial \theta} - \frac{U_\phi\cot\theta}{r} + \frac{1}{r\sin\theta}\frac{\partial U_\theta}{\partial \phi}\right].$$

The problem of determining the displacement **U** is approached on the basis of the uniqueness (Sokolnikoff 1956, Neuber 1934) of the Papkovitch-Neuber stress functions Φ and Ψ, which satisfy the equations

$$\nabla^2\Phi = 0, \qquad \nabla^2\Psi = 0, \tag{14}$$

and which are related to the components of the displacement by the vector equation

$$2G\mathbf{U} = \text{grad}(\Phi + \mathbf{r}.\boldsymbol{\Psi}) - 4(1-\nu)\boldsymbol{\Psi}, \tag{15}$$

where $\mathbf{r}$ is a position vector (i.e. $r^2 = x_i x_i$ in Cartesian coordinates). However, the case under consideration is one of torsionless axi-symmetry, so that it is possible to assume without loss of generality that $\Psi_1 = \Psi_2 = 0$ and $\Psi_3 = \Psi$, in Cartesian coordinates. Equation (15) may therefore be written in the form

$$2G\mathbf{U} = \text{grad}(\Phi + x_3\Psi) - 4(1-\nu)\boldsymbol{\Psi}, \tag{16a}$$

where, in the curvilinear coordinates X_i,

$$\Psi_1 = \frac{\Psi}{h_1}\frac{\partial x_3}{\partial X_1}, \qquad \Psi_2 = \frac{\Psi}{h_2}\frac{\partial x_3}{\partial X_2}, \qquad \Psi_3 = \frac{\Psi}{h_3}\frac{\partial x_3}{\partial X_3}. \tag{16b}$$

In spherical polar coordinates $x_3 = r\cos\theta$ and equations (16) can therefore be written in the form

$$\begin{aligned} 2GU_r &= \frac{\partial\Phi}{\partial r} + r\cos\theta\frac{\partial\Psi}{\partial r} + (4\nu-3)\Psi\cos\theta, \\ 2GU_\theta &= \frac{1}{r}\frac{\partial\Phi}{\partial\theta} + \cos\theta\frac{\partial\Psi}{\partial\theta} - (4\nu-3)\Psi\sin\theta, \\ 2GU_\phi &= 0. \end{aligned} \tag{17}$$

The last result follows either directly from the symmetry of the problem or from the observation that Φ and Ψ can depend only on r and θ. The invariant div $\mathbf{u} = \varepsilon =$ div $\mathbf{U}$ is given, from (16), by

$$\begin{aligned} 2G\varepsilon &= \nabla^2(x_3\Psi) - 4(1-\nu)\,\text{div}\,\boldsymbol{\Psi} \\ &= 2(\text{grad}\,\Psi).(\text{grad}\,x_3) - 4(1-\nu)\,\text{div}\,\boldsymbol{\Psi} \\ &= 2(2\nu-1)\left[\cos\theta\frac{\partial\Psi}{\partial r} - \frac{\sin\theta}{r}\frac{\partial\Psi}{\partial\theta}\right], \end{aligned} \tag{18}$$

so that, from (3a),

$$m_{ij} = 2GE_{ij} + 2\left[\frac{\sin\theta}{r}\frac{\partial\Psi}{\partial\theta} - \cos\theta\frac{\partial\Psi}{\partial r}\right]\nu\,\delta_{ij}. \tag{19}$$

This equation relates the stress components to the strain components, whilst the strain components are given in terms of the displacements by (13) and the displacements are given in terms of the stress functions Φ and Ψ by (17). The boundary condition $m_{ij}n_j = \Lambda^*_i$ with Λ^*_i given by (1) prescribes the values of m_{rr}, $m_{r\theta}$ and $m_{r\phi}$ at the boundary but the value (zero) of the last coefficient is of no interest since $m_{r\phi}$ vanishes identically at all points within the sphere as, incidentally, does $m_{\theta\phi}$. It may readily be shown, using (19), that the boundary conditions of interest are given, at $r = R$, by

$$m_{rr} = \frac{I_s^2}{2\mu_o}\cos^2\theta = \frac{\partial^2\Phi}{\partial r^2} + r\cos\theta\frac{\partial^2\Psi}{\partial r^2} + \frac{2\nu\sin\theta}{r}\frac{\partial\Psi}{\partial\theta} + 2(\nu - 1)\cos\theta\frac{\partial\Psi}{\partial r}, \tag{20a}$$

$$m_{r\theta} = 0 = \frac{1}{r}\frac{\partial^2\Phi}{\partial r\,\partial\theta} + \cos\theta\frac{\partial^2\Psi}{\partial r\,\partial\theta} - \frac{1}{r^2}\frac{\partial\Phi}{\partial\theta} + (1 - 2\nu)\sin\theta\frac{\partial\Psi}{\partial r} - 2(1 - \nu)\frac{\cos\theta}{r}\frac{\partial\Psi}{\partial\theta}. \tag{20b}$$

Since Φ and Ψ are harmonic functions that are independent of ϕ they may be expressed in series form thus:

$$\Phi = \sum_{n=0}^{\infty} \alpha_{2n} r^{2n} P_{2n}, \tag{21a}$$

$$\Psi = \sum_{n=0}^{\infty} \beta_{2n+1} r^{2n+1} P_{2n+1}, \tag{21b}$$

where P_n is the Legendre function $P_n = \mathrm{P}_n(\cos\theta)$ and the choice of even terms in (21a) and odd terms in (21b) is dictated by the requirements

$$\begin{aligned} U_r(r, \pi - \theta) &= U_r(r, \theta), \\ U_\theta(r, \pi - \theta) &= -U_\theta(r, \theta). \end{aligned} \tag{22}$$

However, it may be shown (Problem 1) that the boundary condition (20a) can only be satisfied if all the coefficients α_{2n} and β_{2n+1} are zero except α_2, α_4, β_1 and β_3. With this simplification, equations (20) reduce (Problem 2), on equating coefficients of Legendre functions, to four simultaneous linear equations, which may be solved for α_2, α_4, β_1 and β_3. The corresponding stress functions are given by

$$\begin{aligned} \Phi &= \frac{I_s^2}{2\mu_o}\frac{2(2\nu+3)\nu}{(5\nu+7)(1+\nu)} r^2 P_2 + \frac{I_s^2}{2\mu_o}\frac{4\nu}{3(5\nu+7)R^2} r^4 P_4, \\ \Psi &= -\frac{I_s^2}{2\mu_o}\frac{1}{2(1+\nu)} r P_1 - \frac{I_s^2}{2\mu_o}\frac{7}{3(5\nu+7)R^2} r^3 P_3, \end{aligned} \qquad (23)$$

and when these are substituted into (17) the resulting displacement is identical to that given by equations (8).

The systematic formulation of the problem presented above permits an extension to be made immediately to specimens of more general shape. For example, a prolate spheroid magnetized to saturation along its major axis can be conveniently described (as $\xi = \xi_o$) in the coordinates $X_1 = \xi$, $X_2 = \eta$, $X_3 = \phi$ considered in 4.2(b), with

$$h_1 = h_2 = a(\sinh^2 \xi + \sin^2 \eta)^{\frac{1}{2}}, \qquad h_3 = a \sinh \xi \sin \eta. \qquad (24)$$

Thus, since $x_3 = a \cosh \xi \cos \eta$, equation (18) yields the result

$$2G\varepsilon = \frac{2(2\nu-1)a}{h_1^2}\left[\sinh \xi \cos \eta \frac{\partial \Psi}{\partial \xi} - \cosh \xi \sin \eta \frac{\partial \Psi}{\partial \eta}\right], \qquad (25)$$

so that, from (3a),

$$m_{ij} = 2GE_{ij} + \frac{2a}{h_1^2}\left[\cosh \xi \sin \eta \frac{\partial \Psi}{\partial \eta} - \sinh \xi \cos \eta \frac{\partial \Psi}{\partial \xi}\right] \nu \delta_{ij}. \qquad (26)$$

This equation relates the stress components to the strain components, whilst the strain components are given in terms of the displacements by (10) and the displacements are given in terms of the stress functions Φ and Ψ by (16). Again $\partial\Phi/\partial\phi = 0 = \partial\Psi/\partial\phi$ so that (15) becomes, using the expression for gradient in prolate spheroidal coordinates,

$$2GU_\xi = \frac{1}{h_1}\left[\frac{\partial\Phi}{\partial\xi} + a\cosh\xi\cos\eta\frac{\partial\Psi}{\partial\xi} + (4\nu - 3)a\Psi\sinh\xi\cos\eta\right],$$

$$2GU_\eta = \frac{1}{h_1}\left[\frac{\partial\Phi}{\partial\eta} + a\cosh\xi\cos\eta\frac{\partial\Psi}{\partial\eta} - (4\nu - 3)a\Psi\cosh\xi\sin\eta\right], \tag{27}$$

$$2GU_\phi = 0.$$

As in the case of a sphere, a consideration of the boundary conditions reveals that only two stress components are of interest, namely $m_{\xi\xi}$ and $m_{\xi\eta}$. These may be related to Φ and Ψ by using (25), (26), (27) and (10) to give (Problem 3)

$$\begin{aligned} h_1^2 m_{\xi\xi} = {} & \frac{\partial^2\Phi}{\partial\xi^2} + a\cosh\xi\cos\eta\frac{\partial^2\Psi}{\partial\xi^2} - 2a\sinh\xi\cos\eta\frac{\partial\Psi}{\partial\xi} \\ & + 2\nu a\left[\sinh\xi\cos\eta\frac{\partial\Psi}{\partial\xi} + \cosh\xi\sin\eta\frac{\partial\Psi}{\partial\eta}\right] \\ & + \frac{a^2}{h_1^2}\left[\sin\eta\cos\eta\frac{\partial\Phi}{\partial\eta} - \sinh\xi\cosh\xi\frac{\partial\Phi}{\partial\xi}\right. \\ & \left. + a\sin\eta\cos^2\eta\cosh\xi\frac{\partial\Psi}{\partial\eta} - a\cos\eta\sinh\xi\cosh^2\xi\frac{\partial\Psi}{\partial\xi}\right], \end{aligned} \tag{28a}$$

$$\begin{aligned} h_1^2 m_{\xi\eta} = {} & \frac{\partial^2\Phi}{\partial\xi\,\partial\eta} + \cosh\xi\cos\eta\frac{\partial^2\Psi}{\partial\xi\,\partial\eta} \\ & + (2\nu - 1)a\left[\sinh\xi\cos\eta\frac{\partial\Psi}{\partial\eta} - \cosh\xi\sin\eta\frac{\partial\Psi}{\partial\xi}\right] \\ & - \frac{a^2}{h_1^2}\left[\sin\eta\cos\eta\frac{\partial\Phi}{\partial\xi} + \sinh\xi\cosh\xi\frac{\partial\Phi}{\partial\eta}\right. \\ & \left. + a\sin\eta\cos^2\eta\cosh\xi\frac{\partial\Psi}{\partial\xi} + a\cos\eta\sinh\xi\cosh^2\xi\frac{\partial\Psi}{\partial\eta}\right]. \end{aligned} \tag{28b}$$

It is convenient at this stage to make the substitutions $p = \cos\eta$, $q = \cosh\xi$, so that $q_o = \cosh\xi_o$. Since Φ and Ψ are harmonic functions that are independent of ψ they may be expressed in series form thus:

$$\Phi = \sum_{n=0}^{\infty} \alpha_{2n} P_{2n}(p) P_{2n}(q), \tag{29a}$$

$$\Psi = \sum_{n=0}^{\infty} \beta_{2n+1} P_{2n+1}(p) P_{2n+1}(q), \tag{29b}$$

where the choice of even terms in (29a) and odd terms in (29b) is dictated by the requirements

$$\begin{aligned} U_\xi(\xi, \pi - \eta) &= U_\xi(\xi, \eta), \\ U_\eta(\xi, \pi - \eta) &= -U_\eta(\xi, \eta). \end{aligned} \tag{30}$$

The similarity with the corresponding calculation for the sphere suggests that a solution might be obtained with all the coefficients α_{2n} and β_{2n+1} zero except α_2, α_4, β_1 and β_3, so that

$$\begin{aligned} \Phi &= \alpha_2 P_2(p) P_2(q) + \alpha_4 P_4(p) P_4(q), \\ \Psi &= \beta_1 P_1(p) P_1(q) + \beta_3 P_3(p) P_3(q). \end{aligned} \tag{31}$$

However, these stress functions may be substituted into (28) to obtain $m_{\xi\xi}$ and $m_{\xi\eta}$, which must, at the surface of the spheroid ($\xi = \xi_o$ or $q = q_o$), satisfy the boundary conditions

$$\begin{aligned} h_1^2 m_{\xi\xi} &= \frac{I_s^2}{2\mu_o} \frac{\sinh^2\xi_o \cos^2\eta}{\sinh^2\xi_o + \sin^2\eta} = \frac{I_s^2}{2\mu_o} a^2(q_o^2 - 1)p^2, \\ m_{\xi\eta} &= 0. \end{aligned} \tag{32}$$

This yields (Problem 4) a set of five linear simultaneous equations connecting the four coefficients α_2, α_4, β_1 and β_3: unfortunately, however, these five equations are incompatible, indicating that Φ and/or Ψ must include terms of higher order than P_4. If equations (31) are supplemented by the inclusion of $\beta_5 P_5(p) P_5(q)$ and $\alpha_6 P_6(p) P_6(q)$, then the boundary conditions yield eight simultaneous equations connecting the six coefficients α_2, α_4, α_6, β_1, β_3 and β_5. However, these equations are again incompatible, and it seems probable that the same difficulty will be experienced if terms of even higher order are included. It appears likely, therefore, that the solution involves infinite series and that an analytical solution is impossible. In this case, solutions will only be achieved by numerical methods and an appropriate method of this type is considered in 6.3.

6.3 A numerical method

The most universal numerical method for predicting E^*_{ij} in the ellipsoidal case is the method of finite differences, mentioned in 1.4. In this method differential equations are replaced by finite-difference equations that involve physical conditions at points which are finite in number and regularly spaced. For example, the partial derivatives $\partial\chi/\partial\xi$ and $\partial^2\chi/\partial\xi\,\partial\eta$ of a scalar function, $\chi = \chi(\xi, \eta, \phi)$, which are defined by the equations

$$\frac{\partial \chi}{\partial \xi} = \lim_{k_1 \to 0} \frac{\chi(\xi + k_1, \eta, \phi) - \chi(\xi, \eta, \phi)}{k_1},$$

$$\frac{\partial^2 \chi}{\partial \xi\,\partial \eta} = \lim_{\substack{k_1 \to 0 \\ k_2 \to 0}} \frac{\chi(\xi + k_1, \eta + k_2, \phi) - \chi(\xi + k_1, \eta, \phi) - \chi(\xi, \eta + k_2, \phi) + \chi(\xi, \eta, \phi)}{k_1 k_2}, \tag{33}$$

are approximately equal, for small values of k_1 and k_2, to the difference quotients occurring on the right-hand sides following the limit signs. If substitutions of this type are made in a differential equation the result is a difference equation which is a good approximation to the differential equation when k_1 and k_2 are small. In the difference equation the values of χ are related at a set of discrete points determined by the choice of k_1 and k_2. Usually the points are the intersections of a set of mutually orthogonal straight lines forming a three-dimensional lattice. However, for an ellipsoid, this would necessitate the use of interpolation techniques to deal with the boundary conditions (since the lattice points would not, in general, lie on the boundary). It is preferable therefore to use a curvilinear lattice in which the lines are the coordinate lines of a system of ellipsoidal coordinates. As an example of the method, the prolate spheroid magnetized to saturation along its major axis will again be considered: this case reduces, because of the existence of axial symmetry, to a two-dimensional problem, and the curvilinear lattice is replaced by a curvilinear net.

Consider the cross-sectional plane $\phi = 0$ and a general point of the lattice (ξ_m, η_n), labelled by the two integers m, n, and the eight neighbouring points with coordinates as indicated diagrammatically in Fig. 6.1. With these points labelled as shown it may readily be seen, by analogy with (33), that to the approximation implicit in the finite-difference method

$$\left(\frac{\partial \chi}{\partial \xi}\right)_{m,n} = \frac{\chi_{m+1,n} - \chi_{m-1,n}}{2k_1},$$

$$\left(\frac{\partial^2 \chi}{\partial \xi\, \partial \eta}\right)_{m,n} = \frac{\chi_{m+1,n+1} - \chi_{m+1,n-1} - \chi_{m-1,n+1} + \chi_{m-1,n-1}}{(2k_1)(2k_2)} \tag{34a}$$

and, similarly,

$$\left(\frac{\partial \chi}{\partial \eta}\right)_{m,n} = \frac{\chi_{m,n+1} - \chi_{m,n-1}}{2k_2},$$

$$\left(\frac{\partial^2 \chi}{\partial \eta^2}\right)_{m,n} = \frac{\chi_{m,n+1} - 2\chi_{m,n} + \chi_{m,n-1}}{k_2^2}, \tag{34b}$$

$$\left(\frac{\partial^2 \chi}{\partial \xi^2}\right)_{m,n} = \frac{\chi_{m+1,n} - 2\chi_{m,n} + \chi_{m-1,n}}{k_1^2}.$$

These values may now be substituted into the appropriate differential equation.

It was seen in 6.2 that the displacement **U** is related by (16) to the two Papkovitch-Neuber stress functions Φ and Ψ, which satisfy the differential equations $\nabla^2\Phi = 0 = \nabla^2\Psi$. Although it is possible to solve directly for **U**, the finite-difference equations become cumbersome because the boundary conditions (6) are related to **U** by way of equations (3) and (10). Moreover, since a numerical method is to be used, the fact that Φ and Ψ can be represented as in (21) is of little assistance and it is convenient to work, alternatively, in terms of the stress components m_{ij}. The m_{ij} must satisfy the differential equations (4) and (5) together with the boundary conditions (6). However, the problem is one in which a solid of revolution is loaded so as to maintain axial symmetry after the resulting deformation,

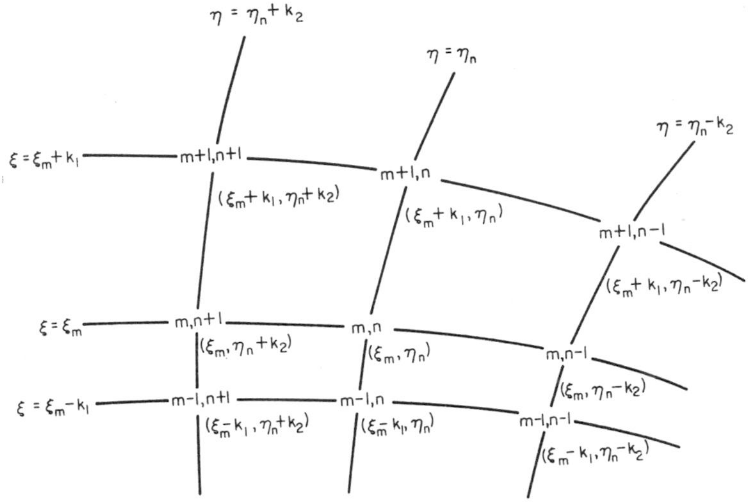

Fig. 6.1

and it may be shown (Southwell 1956) that for such a case the stress components must have the form

$$m_{\rho\rho} = \frac{1}{\rho}\frac{\partial}{\partial\rho}(\psi + \chi) - \frac{1}{\rho^2}[\psi + (1 - \nu)\chi],$$

$$m_{\phi\phi} = \frac{\nu}{\rho}\frac{\partial\chi}{\partial\rho} + \frac{1}{\rho^2}[\psi + (1 - \nu)\chi], \tag{35}$$

$$m_{zz} = -\frac{1}{\rho}\frac{\partial\psi}{\partial\rho}, \qquad m_{\rho\phi} = 0 = m_{\phi z}, \qquad m_{z\rho} = \frac{1}{\rho}\frac{\partial\psi}{\partial z},$$

relative to cylindrical polar coordinates $\overline{X}_1 = \rho$, $\overline{X}_2 = \phi$, $\overline{X}_3 = z$, where $\psi = 0 = \chi$ along the z-axis within the solid and where ψ and

χ satisfy the differential equations

$$\frac{\partial^2\chi}{\partial\rho^2} - \frac{1}{\rho}\frac{\partial\chi}{\partial\rho} + \frac{\partial^2\chi}{\partial z^2} = 0, \tag{36a}$$

$$\frac{\partial^2\psi}{\partial\rho^2} - \frac{1}{\rho}\frac{\partial\psi}{\partial\rho} + \frac{\partial^2\psi}{\partial z^2} = \frac{\partial^2\chi}{\partial z^2}. \tag{36b}$$

Hence, the new stress functions ψ and χ are simply related to the m_{ij} but they are, of course, not necessarily related in a simple way to the displacement. For example, for the sphere magnetized to saturation along the z-axis (Problem 5),

$$\psi = \frac{I_s^2}{8\mu_o(5\nu + 7)R^2}[(\nu + 7)\rho^4 - 2(3\nu + 7)\rho^2 R^2 - 4\nu\rho^2 z^2],$$

$$\chi = \frac{I_s^2}{8\mu_o(1 + \nu)(5\nu + 7)R^2}[-7(1 + \nu)\rho^4 + 2(5\nu + 7)\rho^2 R^2 + 4(8\nu + 7)\rho^2 z^2], \tag{37}$$

whilst the displacement may be obtained by way of equations (35), (3b) and (10).

Before equations (36) may be put into finite-difference form, the partial derivatives with respect to ρ and z must be replaced by derivatives with respect to ξ and η. On comparing the equations $x_1 = \rho\cos\phi$, $x_2 = \rho\sin\phi$, $x_3 = z$ with (16) of 4.2(b) it may be seen that

$$\begin{aligned} \rho &= a\sinh\xi\sin\eta, \\ z &= a\cosh\xi\cos\eta. \end{aligned} \tag{38}$$

The partial derivates with respect to $X_1 = \xi$, $X_2 = \eta$ may be readily expressed in terms of the partial derivatives with respect to $\overline{X}_1 = \rho$, $\overline{X}_3 = z$ by

$$\frac{\partial}{\partial X_i} = \frac{\partial \overline{X}_j}{\partial X_i}\frac{\partial}{\partial \overline{X}_j}, \tag{39}$$

E.M.F.—L

a set of equations which, upon inversion, yields

$$J^2 \frac{\partial}{\partial \rho} = a \cosh \xi \sin \eta \frac{\partial}{\partial \xi} + a \sinh \xi \cos \eta \frac{\partial}{\partial \eta},$$

$$J^2 \frac{\partial}{\partial z} = a \sinh \xi \cos \eta \frac{\partial}{\partial \xi} - a \cosh \xi \sin \eta \frac{\partial}{\partial \eta}, \tag{40a}$$

where

$$J^2 = a^2(\cosh^2 \xi - \cos^2 \eta). \tag{40b}$$

Hence equations (36a) and (36b) may be expressed (after multiplication by J^2 and by J^6 respectively) in the forms

$$\frac{\partial^2 \chi}{\partial \xi^2} - \coth \xi \frac{\partial \chi}{\partial \xi} - \cot \eta \frac{\partial \chi}{\partial \eta} + \frac{\partial^2 \chi}{\partial \eta^2} = 0, \tag{41a}$$

$$\begin{aligned} J^4 \left[\frac{\partial^2 \psi}{\partial \xi^2} - \coth \xi \frac{\partial \psi}{\partial \xi} - \cot \eta \frac{\partial \psi}{\partial \eta} + \frac{\partial^2 \psi}{\partial \eta^2} \right] \\ = J^2 \Bigg[a^2 \sinh^2 \xi \cos^2 \eta \frac{\partial^2 \chi}{\partial \xi^2} - 2a^2 \sinh \xi \cosh \xi \sin \eta \cos \eta \frac{\partial^2 \chi}{\partial \xi \, \partial \eta} \\ + a^2 \cosh^2 \xi \sin^2 \eta \frac{\partial^2 \chi}{\partial \eta^2} \Bigg] \\ + a^2 \sinh \xi \cosh \xi [J^2 - 2a^2 \cos^2 \eta (\sinh^2 \xi - \sin^2 \eta)] \frac{\partial \chi}{\partial \xi} \\ + a^2 \sin \eta \cos \eta [J^2 + 2a^2 \cosh^2 \xi (\sinh^2 \xi - \sin^2 \eta)] \frac{\partial \chi}{\partial \eta}. \end{aligned} \tag{41b}$$

The result of writing these equations in finite-difference form, using (34) and a similar set of equations with ψ replacing χ, is

$$\begin{aligned} \left[-\frac{2}{k_1^2} - \frac{2}{k_2^2} \right] \chi_{m,n} + \left[\frac{1}{k_2^2} - \frac{\cot(nk_2)}{2k_2} \right] \chi_{m,n+1} + \left[\frac{1}{k_2^2} + \frac{\cot(nk_2)}{2k_2} \right] \chi_{m,n-1} \\ + \left[\frac{1}{k_1^2} - \frac{\coth(mk_1)}{2k_1} \right] \chi_{m+1,n} + \left[\frac{1}{k_1^2} + \frac{\coth(mk_1)}{2k_1} \right] \chi_{m-1,n} = 0, \end{aligned} \tag{42a}$$

$$J_{m,n}^4\left\{\left[-\frac{2}{k_1^2}-\frac{2}{k_2^2}\right]\psi_{m,n}+\left[\frac{1}{k_2^2}-\frac{\cot(nk_2)}{2k_2}\right]\psi_{m,n+1}+\left[\frac{1}{k_2^2}+\frac{\cot(nk_2)}{2k_2}\right]\psi_{m,n-1}\right.$$

$$\left.+\left[\frac{1}{k_1^2}-\frac{\coth(mk_1)}{2k_1}\right]\psi_{m+1,n}+\left[\frac{1}{k_1^2}+\frac{\coth(mk_1)}{2k_1}\right]\psi_{m-1,n}\right\}$$

$$=J_{m,n}^2\left[-\frac{2a^2\sinh^2(mk_1)\cos^2(nk_2)}{k_1^2}-\frac{2a^2\cosh^2(mk_1)\sin^2(nk_2)}{k_2^2}\right]\chi_{m,n}$$

$$+\left\{J_{m,n}^2\left[\frac{a^2\cosh^2(mk_1)\sin^2(nk_2)}{k_2^2}+\frac{a^2\sin(nk_2)\cos(nk_2)}{2k_2}\right]\right.$$

$$\left.+\frac{2a^4\sin(nk_2)\cos(nk_2)\cosh^2(mk_1)[\sinh^2(mk_1)-\sin^2(nk_2)]}{2k_2}\right\}\chi_{m,n+1}$$

$$+\left\{J_{m,n}^2\left[\frac{a^2\cosh^2(mk_1)\sin^2(nk_2)}{k_2^2}-\frac{a^2\sin(nk_2)\cos(nk_2)}{2k_2}\right]\right.$$

$$\left.-\frac{2a^4\sin(nk_2)\cos(nk_2)\cosh^2(mk_1)[\sinh^2(mk_1)-\sin^2(nk_2)]}{2k_2}\right\}\chi_{m,n-1}$$

$$+\left\{J_{m,n}^2\left[\frac{a^2\sinh^2(mk_1)\cos^2(nk_2)}{k_1^2}+\frac{a^2\sinh(mk_1)\cosh(mk_1)}{2k_1}\right]\right.$$

$$\left.-\frac{2a^4\sinh(mk_1)\cosh(mk_1)\cos^2(nk_2)[\sinh^2(mk_1)-\sin^2(nk_2)]}{2k_1}\right\}\chi_{m+1,n}$$

$$+\left\{J_{m,n}^2\left[\frac{a^2\sinh^2(mk_1)\cos^2(nk_2)}{k_1^2}-\frac{a^2\sinh(mk_1)\cosh(mk_1)}{2k_1}\right]\right.$$

$$\left.+\frac{2a^4\sinh(mk_1)\cosh(mk_1)\cos^2(nk_2)[\sinh^2(mk_1)-\sin^2(nk_2)]}{2k_1}\right\}\chi_{m-1,n}$$

$$+J_{m,n}^2\left[-\frac{2a^2\sinh(mk_1)\cosh(mk_1)\sin(nk_2)\cos(nk_2)}{4k_1k_2}\right]\chi_{m+1,n+1}$$

$$+J_{m,n}^2\left[\frac{2a^2\sinh(mk_1)\cosh(mk_1)\sin(nk_2)\cos(nk_2)}{4k_1k_2}\right]\chi_{m+1,n-1}$$

$$+J_{m,n}^2\left[\frac{2a^2\sinh(mk_1)\cosh(mk_1)\sin(nk_2)\cos(nk_2)}{4k_1k_2}\right]\chi_{m-1,n+1}$$

$$+J_{m,n}^2\left[-\frac{2a^2\sinh(mk_1)\cosh(mk_1)\sin(nk_2)\cos(nk_2)}{4k_1k_2}\right]\chi_{m-1,n-1}\,. \qquad (42b)$$

The boundary conditions on the stress components are $m_{ij}n_j = \Lambda_i^*$ or, in cylindrical polar coordinates,

$$
\begin{aligned}
m_{\rho\rho}\sin\gamma + m_{\rho z}\cos\gamma &= \Lambda_\rho^* = \frac{I_s^2}{2\mu_o}\cos^2\gamma\sin\gamma\,,\\
m_{z\rho}\sin\gamma + m_{zz}\cos\gamma &= \Lambda_z^* = \frac{I_s^2}{2\mu_o}\cos^3\gamma\,,
\end{aligned}
\tag{43}
$$

where γ is the angle between $\mathbf{n}$ and the z-axis. Moreover, the intersection of the surface of the spheroid ($\xi = \xi_o$) and the plane $\phi = 0$ (or $x_2 = 0$) is the ellipse

$$
\frac{x_1^2}{a^2\sinh^2\xi_o} + \frac{x_3^2}{a^2\cosh^2\xi_o} = 1\,, \tag{44}
$$

so that

$$
\tan\gamma = -\frac{dx_3}{dx_1} = \frac{x_1\cosh^2\xi_o}{x_3\sinh^2\xi_o} = \coth\xi_o\tan\eta\,. \tag{45}
$$

Hence (43) may be written in the form

$$
\begin{aligned}
m_{\rho\rho}\coth\xi_o\tan\eta + m_{z\rho} &= \frac{I_s^2}{2\mu_o}\,\frac{a^2\sinh\xi_o\cosh\xi_o\sin\eta\cos\eta}{J_o^2}\,,\\
m_{z\rho}\coth\xi_o\tan\eta + m_{zz} &= \frac{I_s^2}{2\mu_o}\,\frac{a^2\sinh^2\xi_o\cos^2\eta}{J_o^2}\,,
\end{aligned}
\tag{46}
$$

where $J_o^2 = a^2(\cosh\xi_o - \cos^2\eta)$. When the stress components are replaced by the expressions given by (35), these boundary conditions become (for $\xi = \xi_o$)

$$
J_o^2 a_1\frac{\partial\psi}{\partial\xi} + a_1a_3^2\sin^2\eta\,\frac{\partial\chi}{\partial\xi} + a_1^2a_3\sin\eta\cos\eta\,\frac{\partial\chi}{\partial\eta} - J_o^2a_3[\psi + (1-\nu)\chi]
$$

$$
= \frac{I_s^2}{2\mu_o}\,a_1^4a_3\sin^2\eta\cos^2\eta\,, \tag{47}
$$

$$
J_o^2\frac{\partial\psi}{\partial\eta} = -\frac{I_s^2}{2\mu_o}\,a_1^4\sin\eta\cos^3\eta\,, \tag{48}
$$

with $a_1 = a\sinh\xi_o$ and $a_3 = a\cosh\xi_o$, as in 4.2(b). Since ψ is zero along the z-axis within the solid, it is zero at the points $(\xi_o, 0)$ and

(ξ_o, π), so that integration of (48) around the bounding ellipse $\xi = \xi_o$ gives

$$\psi = \frac{I_s^2}{4\mu_o}\frac{a_1^4}{a^4}\left[a^2 \sin^2 \eta + a_3^2 \ln\left(\frac{a_3^2 - a^2}{a_3^2 - a^2 \cos^2 \eta}\right)\right]. \tag{49}$$

The boundary conditions are therefore given by equations (47) and (49), or by

$$J^2_{m_o,n}\frac{a_1}{2k_1}(\psi_{m_o+1,n} - \psi_{m_o-1,n}) + \frac{a_1 a_3^2 \sin^2 (nk^2)}{2k_1}(\chi_{m_o+1,n} - \chi_{m_o-1,n})$$

$$+\frac{a_1^2 a_3 \sin (nk_2) \cos (nk_2)}{2k_2}(\chi_{m_o,n+1} - \chi_{m_o,n-1})$$

$$- J^2_{m_o,n} a_3 [\psi_{m_o,n} + (1 - \nu)\chi_{m_o,n}]$$

$$= \frac{I_s^2}{2\mu_o} a_1^4 a_3 \sin^2 (nk_2) \cos^2 (nk_2), \tag{50a}$$

$$\psi_{m,n} = \frac{I_s^2}{4\mu_o}\frac{a_1^4}{a^4}\left[a^2 \sin^2 (nk_2) + a_3^2 \ln\left(\frac{a_3^2 - a^2}{a_3^2 - a^2 \cos^2 (nk_2)}\right)\right], \tag{50b}$$

and since (50a) applies to points on the boundary ($m = m_o$) it must involve the values of ψ and χ at additional points $(m_o + 1, n)$ just outside the solid material. This is permissible provided the number of unknowns is not thereby caused to exceed the number of equations.

If the range $0 \leqslant \xi \leqslant \xi_o$ is divided into $r - 1$ intervals and the range $0 \leqslant \eta \leqslant \pi$ is divided into $s - 1$ intervals, then there are $r + 1$ lattice points, or nodes, on a line of constant η in the curvilinear net—including the additional point $(m_o + 1, n)$—whilst there are s nodes on a coordinate line of constant ξ. There are thus $(r + 1)s$ unknown values of the function ψ and an equal number for χ. The boundary condition $\psi = 0$ along the z-axis provides s values of ψ within the range $\xi = 0$, $0 \leqslant \eta \leqslant \pi$, a *further* r values within the range $\eta = 0$, $0 \leqslant \xi \leqslant \xi_o + k_1$ and a further r values within the range $\eta = \pi$, $0 \leqslant \xi \leqslant \xi_o + k_1$. This boundary condition thus prescribes ψ at $2r + s$ nodes and, when the corresponding condition on χ is considered, $2(2r + s)$ values of the stress functions are prescribed. Similarly (50a) and (50b) each provide $s-2$ equations prescribing or connecting the values of the stress functions at $s - 2$

further nodes, whilst (42a) and (42b) each provides $(r - 1)(s - 2)$ equations connecting stress functions at $(r - 1)(s - 2)$ further nodes. In total, therefore, there are $2s(r + 1)$ equations connecting the values of ψ and χ at $s(r + 1)$ nodes, i.e. all the nodes within the region considered. The problem has therefore been formulated in such a way that approximate solutions for ψ and χ can be obtained either by relaxation techniques or, preferably, by direct solution of the $2s(r + 1)$ linear simultaneous equations, using a high-speed digital computer. The degree of accuracy obtainable depends, of course, on the size of r and s. As an example, Fig. 6.2 shows a comparison

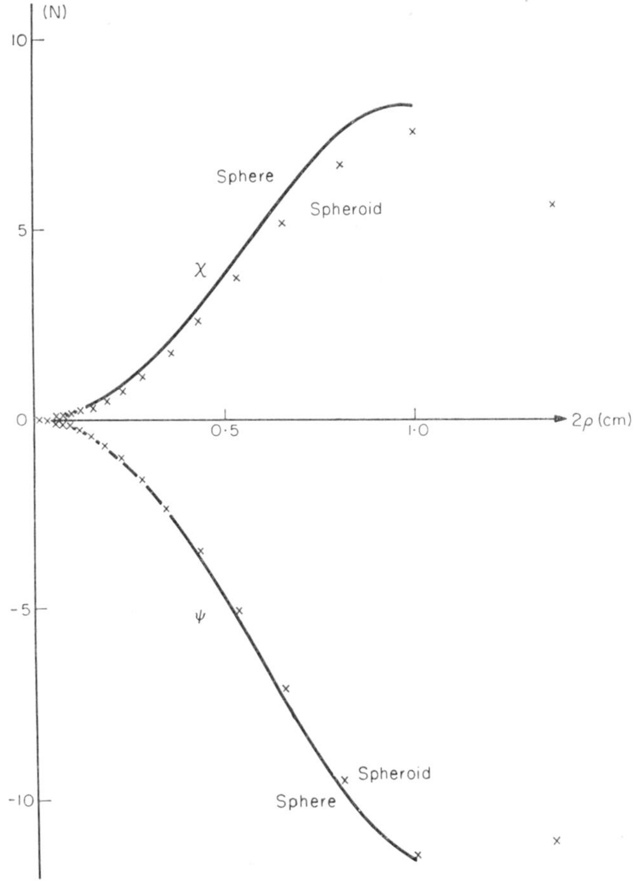

Fig. 6.2

between the values of ψ and χ for a sphere, given by (37), and the values obtained for a prolate spheroid of axial ratio 0.999 using $r = s = 20$. The numerical calculation was performed on an I.C.T. 1905 computer using the values $2R = 1$ cm, $I_s = 2.15$ Weber m^{-2} and $\nu = 0.3$, which gave the points shown in Fig. 6.2: the full curves are the analytical solutions given by (37) with $z = 0$.

PROBLEMS 6

1. Substitute (21) in (20a) and evaluate the derivates to obtain an expression for m_{rr} in terms of odd and even Legendre functions. Eliminate the odd functions by using the recurrence relationship

$$\cos\theta\, P_m = \frac{m+1}{2m+1}P_{m+1} + \frac{m}{2m+1}P_{m-1}$$

and, by equating the resulting expression to $(2P_2 + P_o)I_s^2/6\mu_o$ at $r = R$, establish that all the coefficients α_{2n} and β_{2n+1} are zero except α_2, α_4, β_1 and β_3.

2. Substitute (21) in (20b) and use the result established in Problem 1 together with the recurrence relationship

$$\sin\theta\frac{dP_m}{d\theta} = \frac{m(m+1)}{2m+1}(P_{m+1} - P_{m-1})$$

to express $m_{r\theta}$ in terms of odd Legendre functions. Hence use the boundary conditions at $r = R$ to derive four simultaneous equations that have (23) as solutions.

3. Verify from equation (10) that for a prolate spheroid

$$E_{\xi\xi} = \frac{\partial}{\partial\xi}\left[\frac{U_\xi}{h_1}\right] + \frac{1}{2h_1^2}\left[\frac{U_\xi}{h_1}\frac{\partial h_1^2}{\partial\xi} + \frac{U_\eta}{h_1}\frac{\partial h_1^2}{\partial\eta}\right],$$

$$E_{\xi\eta} = \tfrac{1}{2}\frac{\partial}{\partial\xi}\left[\frac{U_\eta}{h_1}\right] + \tfrac{1}{2}\frac{\partial}{\partial\eta}\left[\frac{U_\xi}{h_1}\right],$$

and use equations (25), (26) and (27) to confirm that $m_{\xi\xi}$ and $m_{\xi\eta}$ are given by (28).

4. Replace the derivatives with respect to ξ and η in (28) by derivatives with respect to p and q; then use (29) with only α_2, α_4, β_1 and β_3 non-zero to show that the boundary conditions (32) are equivalent to the (incompatible) simultaneous equations

$$-24q_o^2\alpha 2 + 15q_o^2(21q_o^2 - 17)\alpha_4 - 32vaq_o^2\beta_1 + 24vaq_o^2(5q_o^2 - 3)\beta_3 = 0,$$

$$12(3q_o^2 - 2)\alpha_2 + 15(-105q_o^4 + 99q_o^2 - 10)\alpha_4 + 16a[(2v - 1)q_o^2 + (1 - v)]\beta_1 - 12a[45vq_o^4 + (8 - 36v)q_o^2 + 3(v - 1)]\beta_3 = \frac{4I_s^2a^2}{\mu_o}(q_o^2 - 1),$$

$$7(35q_o^4 - 35q_o^2 + 4)\alpha_4 + 8a[10vq_o^4 + (2 - 9v)q_o^2 + (v - 1)]\beta_3 = 0,$$

$$72\alpha_2 + 15(37 - 105q_o^2)\alpha_4 + 32(2v - 1)a\beta_1 + 24a[(6v - 3) + 5(1 - 4v)q_o^2]\beta_3 = 0,$$

$$35(7q_o^2 - 3)\alpha_4 + 8a(1 - 4v + 10vq_o^2)\beta_3 = 0.$$

5. Use the matrix corresponding to a positive rotation ϕ about the x_3-axis to transform the stress components given by (7) into the components relative to cylindrical polar coordinates (ρ, ϕ, z). Verify that a comparison with (35) yields four simultaneous equations for ψ, χ, $\partial\psi/\partial\rho$, $\partial\chi/\partial\rho$ and $\partial\psi/\partial z$ that may be solved to give (37).

REFERENCES

Abraham, M. and Becker, R. (1950). *Electricity and Magnetism*. Blackie.
Allen, D. N. de G. (1954). *Relaxation Methods*. McGraw-Hill.
Anderholm, N. C. and Peck, E. R. (1965). *J. Appl. Phys.*, **36**, 2293.

Becker, R. (1934). *Z. Phys.*, **87**, 547.
Becker, R. and Döring, W. (1939). *Ferromagnetismus*. Springer, Berlin.
Bewley, L. V. (1948). *Two-dimensional Fields in Electrical Engineering*. Macmillan, New York.
Binns, K. J. and Lawrenson, P. J. (1963). *Analysis and Computation of Electric and Magnetic Field Problems*. Pergamon.
Birss, R. R. (1964). *Symmetry and Magnetism*. North-Holland Publishing Company, Amsterdam.
Birss, R. R. (1959). *Advances in Physics*, **8**, 252.
Birss, R. R. (1960). *Proc. Phys. Soc.*, **75**, 8.
Birss, R. R. (1967). *Proc. Phys. Soc.*, **90**, 453.
Birss, R. R. and Anderson, J. C. (1963). *Proc. Phys. Soc.*, **18**, 1139.
Birss, R. R. and Hegarty, B. C. (1966). *Brit. J. Appl. Phys.*, **17**, 1241.
Birss, R. R., Hegarty, B. C. and Wallis, P. M. (1967). *Brit. J. Appl. Phys.*, **18**, 459.
Bozorth, R. M. (1951). *Ferromagnetism*. Van Nostrand.
Brown, W. F. (1962). *Magnetostatic Principles in Ferromagnetism*. North-Holland, Amsterdam.
Brown, W. F. (1951). *Am. J. Phys.*, **19**, 290 and 333.

Caldonazzo, B. (1932). *Rend. della R. Acc. Naz. dei Lincei*, **15**, 840.
Carpenter, C. J. (1959). *Proc. I.E.E.*, **107C**, 19.
Chu, L. J., Haus, H. A. and Penfield, P. (1966). *Proc. I.E.E.E.*, **54**, 920.
Coulson, C. A. (1953). *Electricity*, 3rd edn. Oliver and Boyd.

Diggle, H. and Harthill, E. R. (1954). *Proc. I.E.E.*, **101**, II, p. 349.
Durand, E. (1953). *Electrostatique et Magnétostatique*. Masson, Paris.

Eringen, A. C. (1962). *Nonlinear Theory of Continuous Media*, McGraw-Hill.

Gersdorf, R. (1960). *Physica*, **26**, 553.
Gersdorf, R., Stoelinga, J. H. M. and Rathenau, G. W. (1961). *Physica*, **27**, 381.

Hague, B. (1929). *Electromagnetic Problems in Electrical Engineering*, Oxford University Press.
Hakim, S. S. (1962). *Proc. I.E.E.*, **109**, 158.
Hammond, P. (1966). *Proc. I.E.E.*, **113**, 401.
Hughes, D. J. (1953). *Pile Neutron Research*. Addison-Wesley, Cambridge, Massachusetts, pp. 282, and 302 to 305.

Jackson, J. D. (1962). *Classical Electrodynamics*. Wiley.
Jaynes, E. T. (1953). *Ferroelectricity*. Princeton University Press.
Jeans, J. (1927). *The Mathematical Theory of Electricity and Magnetism*. Cambridge University Press.
Jeffreys, H. (1961). *Cartesian Tensors*. Cambridge University Press.

References

KELLOGG, O. (1929). *Foundations of Potential Theory*. Springer, Berlin.
KITTEL, C. (1956). *Introduction to Solid State Physics*, 2nd edn. Wiley, New York. Chapman and Hall, London.

LAWTON, H. and STEWART, K. H. (1948). *Proc. Roy. Soc. A*, **193,** 72.
LEATHAM, J. G. (1913). *Volume and Surface Integrals used in Physics*, 2nd edn. Cambridge University Press.
LEE, E. W. (1953). *Sci. Prog.*, **161**, 58.
LEE, E. W. (1955). *Rep. Prog. Phys.*, **18**, 184.
LORENTZ, H. A. (1909). *The Theory of Electrons*. Teubner, Leipzig.
LOVE, A. E. H. (1944). *A Treatise on the Mathematical Theory of Elasticity*, 4th edn. Cambridge University Press.

MACROBERT, T. M. (1927). *Spherical Harmonics*. Methuen.
MASON, M. and WEAVER, W. (1929). *The Electromagnetic Field*. University of Chicago Press.
MAXWELL, J. C. (1873). *Treatise on Electricity and Magnetism*. Oxford University Press.
MORRISH, A. H. (1965). *The Physical Principles of Magnetism*. Wiley.

NEÉL, L. (1944). *J. Phys. Radium*, **5**, 241.
NEUBER, H. (1934). *Zeit. f. angewandte Math. und Mech.*, **14**, 203.
NEWTON, I. (1687). *Philosophiae Naturalis Principia Mathematica*, London, 3rd edn.

ONSAGER, L. (1936). *J. Am. Chem. Soc.*, **58**, 1486.
O'RAHILLY, A. (1938). *Electromagnetics*. Longmans, London. University Press, Cork.
OSBORN, J. A. (1945). *Phys. Rev.*, **67**, 351.

PAGE, L. and ADAMS, N. I. (1940). *Electrodynamics*. Van Nostrand.
PANOFSKY, W. K. H. and PHILLIPS, M. (1955). *Classical Electricity and Magnetism*. Addison-Wesley, Reading, Massachusetts.
PASTORI, M. (1930). *Rend. della R. Acc. Naz. dei Lincei*, **12**, 499.
PENFIELD, P. and HAUS, H. A. (1966). *Phys. Fluids*, **9**, 1195.
PIERCE, B. O. (1929). *A Short Table of Integrals*, 3rd edn. Ginn, New York, p. 66 et seq.
POCKELS, F. (1906). *Encyklopadie der mathematischen Wissenschaften*, vol. V, part II. Teubner, Leipzig.
POINCARÉ, H. (1892). *Lecons sur la théorie de l'élasticité*. Paris.
POWELL, F. C. (1931). *Proc. Camb. Phil. Soc.*, **27**, 561.

ROSENFELD, L. (1951). *Theory of Electrons*. North-Holland Publishing Co., Amsterdam

SANDARS, P. G. H. (1966). *Contemporary Physics*, **7**, 419.
SHAW, F. S. (1953). *An Introduction to Relaxation Methods*. Dover, New York.
SLATER, J. C. (1950). *Phys. Rev.*, **78**, 748.
SLEPIAN, J. (1950). *Proc. Natl. Acad. Sci., U.S.*, **36**, 485.
SOKOLNIKOFF, I. S. (1956). *Mathematical Theory of Elasticity*, 2nd edn. McGraw-Hill.
SOUTHWELL, R. V. (1940). *Relaxation Methods in Engineering Science*. Oxford University Press. (1946 and 1956). *Relaxation Methods in Theoretical Physics* (in two parts), Oxford University Press.
SOUTHWELL, R. V. (1929). 'Mechanics', *Encycl. Britt.* 14th edn.
STONER, E C. (1945). *Phil. Mag.*, **36**, 803.
STRATTON, J. A. (1941). *Electromagnetic Theory*. McGraw-Hill.

References

THOMSON, W. and TAIT, P. G. (1883). *Treatise on Natural Philosophy*, 2nd edn. Cambridge University Press.

TOUPIN, R. A. (1956). *J. Rat. Mech. Anal.*, **5**, 849.

TOUPIN, R. A. (1963). *Int. J. Eng. Sci.*, **1**, 101.

TRUESDELL, C. and TOUPIN, R. (1960). The Classical Field Theories, *Handbuch der Physik*, vol. III/1, Springer, Berlin.

TUSTIN, A. (1952). *Direct Current Machines for Control Systems*. Spon.

VAN VLECK, J. H. (1932). *The Theory of Electric and Magnetic Susceptibilities*. Oxford University Press.

VLADIMIRSKY, K. V. (1943). *C. R. Acad. Sci., U.R.S.S.*, **41**, 10.

WEBER, E. (1950). *Electromagnetic Fields*, vol. I. *Mapping of Fields*. Wiley.

WEBSTER, A. G. (1925). *The Dynamics of Particles and of Rigid, Elastic and Fluid Boldies*, 3rd edn. Teubner, Leipzig.

Index

Index

Index